CITY OF LIVERPOOL COMMUNITY COLLEGE

AAT

and

Intermediate

NVQ Level 3

Unit 7 - Preparing reports and returns

Unit 8 - Preparing VAT returns

WORKBOOK

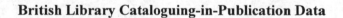

British Library Cataloguing-in-Publication Data

A catalogue record for this book is available from the British Library.

Published by AT Foulks Lynch Ltd
Number 4
The Griffin Centre
Staines Road
Feltham
Middlesex
TW14 0HS

ISBN 0 7483 3492 0

Acknowledgements

CONTENTS

PREFACE

This is the new edition of the AAT NVQ workbook for Units 7 and 8. The two units are covered together in one workbook because of the very large amount of overlap between the subjects.

The workbook has been produced to complement our Units 7 and 8 textbook and it contains numerous practice questions and tasks designed to reflect and simulate the work place environment. These are arranged to match the chapters of the textbook, so that you can work through the two books together.

The workbook also contains practice devolved and central assessments to prepare you completely for the assessment procedures which form part of your course.

Fully comprehensive answers to all questions, tasks and assessments are provided, with the exception of those which are designated as being specifically for classroom work.

You will find that completion of all the elements of this workbook will prepare you admirably for the assessments which you must carry out to pass Units 7 and 8.

Practice Central Assessment Activities

We include a section of Practice Central Assessment Activities which comprises tasks and questions from recent AAT Central Assessments. This provides an excellent preparation for students as they approach their Central Assessment. We have used the Official answers provided by the AAT because the AAT have indicated that that is their preference as these answers show the correct depth that students should achieve.

Class Activities and Assessments

A feature of this workbook is the section at the end comprising Activities and Assessments which are specially designed for classroom use. The answers to these are not included in the workbook but are available to college lecturers who use the workbooks.

Activities are provided for each of the chapters of the workbook and in addition there are two Practice Devolved Assessments and a Practice Central Assessment.

QUESTIONS

UNIT 7

PREPARING REPORTS
AND RETURNS

CHAPTER 1

QUESTIONS

BASIC MATHEMATICAL TECHNIQUES

Activity 1

Given $s_1 = 4$, $s_2 = 3$, $s_3 = 6$, $s_4 = 5$, $s_5 = 4$ and $t_1 = 5$, $t_2 = 4$, $t_3 = 1$, $t_4 = 2$, $t_5 = 6$

Task

Calculate:

(i) Σs
(ii) Σt
(iii) Σst
(iv) $\Sigma s \Sigma t$

Activity 2

Task

Calculate a weighted average of the following prices, using the quantities sold as weights:

Price (£)	Quantity sold
10	50
12	100
14	40
16	20

Activity 3

A contribution statement has been produced for two products manufactured by Xtra Ltd.

	Product A			Product B		
	Budget £	Actual £	% Change	Budget £	Actual £	% Change
Sales	98,000	103,000		14,000	20,000	
Material costs	(34,000)	(39,000)		(4,600)	(7,200)	
Labour costs	(24,200)	(23,600)		(2,650)	(2,650)	
Overheads	(24,200)	(20,000)		(2,650)	(3,400)	
Contribution	15,600	20,400		4,100	6,750	

Task

Show the percentage changes in the columns provided.

CHAPTER 2

QUESTIONS

TABULATION OF DATA

Activity 1

Alpha Products plc has two departments, A and B. The total wage bill in 19X7 was £513,000, of which £218,000 was for department A and the rest for department B. The corresponding figures for 19X8 were £537,000 and £224,000. The number employed in department A was 30 in 19X7 and decreased by five for the next year. The number employed in department B was 42 in 19X7 and increased by one for the year 19X8.

Task

Tabulate this data to bring out the changes over the two-year period for each department and the company as a whole.

Activity 2

The following information has been provided by Waterson plc:

In the property division, for the year ended 31 March 19X9, pre-tax profits were £15,426,000 compared with £12,141,000 for the previous year. Earnings per share were 29.62 pence, compared with 24.10 pence in the previous year, and dividends per share were 13.50 pence compared with 11.52 pence for the previous year.

In the manufacturing division for the same periods, pre-tax profits were £9,271,000 compared with £8,343,000, earnings per share were 15.75 pence compared with 14.91 pence, and dividends were 9.63 pence per share compared with 8.86 pence.

Task 1

Put this data into tabular form, including any helpful secondary statistics.

Task 2

Comment on what the table shows about the performance of this company.

Activity 3

Fifty university students were selected at random and their heights were measured in inches. The following values were found and recorded:

67	71	61	70	66
68	72	71	76	72
77	71	66	70	72
71	64	70	72	66
70	67	71	66	69
73	74	68	70	73
67	69	69	70	71
69	74	68	72	70
70	65	69	75	67
72	70	68	73	67

Task

Using the data given, construct a grouped frequency distribution of the university students' heights.

Activity 4

The price of the ordinary 25p shares of Manco plc quoted on the Stock Exchange at the close of business on successive Fridays is tabulated below:

126	120	122	105	129	119	131	138
125	127	113	112	130	122	134	136
128	126	117	114	120	123	127	140
124	127	114	111	116	131	128	137
127	122	106	121	116	135	142	130

Task

Group the above data into eight classes.

Activity 5

The United Kingdom's merchant shipping fleet of vessels of 500 gross tonnes and over in April 19X5 consisted of:

Type	Number of vessels	Gross tonnage ('000)
Passenger vessels	85	626
Tankers	257	6,812
Cargo liners	97	876
Container vessels	55	1,559
Tramps	167	352
Bulk carriers	80	3,109

In April 19X3, the figures were:

Passenger vessels	86	573
Tankers	329	10,030
Cargo liners	134	1,194
Container vessels	64	1,613
Tramps	190	406
Bulk carriers	128	4,709

Task

Set out the foregoing information in the form of a table adding such derived statistics as you consider relevant.

Activity 6

A sample of 12 packets taken from an automatic filling machine had the following weights in kilograms:

504, 506, 501, 505, 507, 506, 504, 508, 503, 505, 502, 504

Task 1

Find.

(a) The median weight.
(b) The modal weight.
(c) The arithmetic mean weight.

Task 2

Calculate the geometric mean of the lowest and highest weights.

Task 3

Find the effect on the median, mode and arithmetic mean if one extra value of 495 were included.

Activity 7

The production of each manufacturing department of your company is monitored weekly to establish productivity bonuses paid to members of that department.

250 items have to be produced each week before a bonus will be paid. The production of one department over a forty week period is shown below:

382	367	364	365	371	370	372	364	355	347
354	359	359	360	357	362	364	365	371	365
361	380	382	394	396	398	402	406	437	456
469	466	459	454	460	457	452	451	445	446

Task 1

Form a frequency distribution of five groups for the number of items produced per week.

Task 2

Construct the ogive or cumulative frequency diagram for the frequency distribution established in Task 1.

Task 3

Establish the value of the median from the ogive.

Task 4

Contrast the use of the median and the mean as measures of location.

Activity 8

A frequency distribution of a sample of incomes is as follows:

£	Frequency
40 and less than 80	7
80 and less than 100	16
100 and less than 120	28
120 and less than 130	21
130 and less than 140	8
	80

In the histogram of this data, the rectangle for the £80–£100 class has a height of 8 cm.

Task

What should be the height of the rectangles for the following classes:

(a)   £100 to 120?

(b)   £130 to 140?

Activity 9

Task

From the following data prepare:

(a)   a histogram;

(b)   a frequency polygon; and

(c)   an ogive.

Height of students (inches)	Number of students
$\geq 60 < 63$	5
$\geq 63 < 66$	18
$\geq 66 < 69$	42
$\geq 69 < 72$	27
$\geq 72 < 75$	8
	100

Activity 10

The following table shows the heights of a sample of 100 cabinets. Calculate the arithmetic mean.

Class interval Height (cms)	Frequency f
$\geq 150 < 160$	1
$\geq 160 < 170$	9
$\geq 170 < 180$	12
$\geq 180 < 190$	16
$\geq 190 < 200$	26
$\geq 200 < 210$	19
$\geq 210 < 220$	8
$\geq 220 < 230$	6
$\geq 230 < 240$	2
$\geq 240 < 250$	1
	$\Sigma f = 100$

Activity 11

Find the median of the data from Activity 10.

Activity 12

Find the mode for the data in Activity 10 using an appropriate formula.

CHAPTER 3

QUESTIONS

DIAGRAMMATIC PRESENTATION

Activity 1

The following data has been extracted from the annual report of a manufacturing company:

	Annual sales (£ million)	
	19X8	*19X7*
United Kingdom	35.0	31.5
EC (other than UK)	47.4	33.2
North America	78.9	40.3
Australia	18.2	26.1

Task

Represent this data by component bar charts.

Activity 2

A department store has three departments, as listed below, together with the sales for the years 19X5, 19X6 and 19X7.

	Sales (£'000,000)		
Department	*19X5*	*19X6*	*19X7*
Furnishing	5	6	8
Clothing	12	15	19
Hardware	3	4	4

Task

Construct multiple bar charts to represent the data over the three years.

Activity 3

For the years 19X6 and 19X7 an analysis of sales by destination is given as:

	Sales in 19X6 £'000	*Sales in 19X7 £'000*
United Kingdom	1,760	1,800
EC countries (other than UK)	576	612
Other European countries	214	374
North and South America	306	354
CIS	54	72
Other overseas countries	127	584

Task

Draw comparative pie charts illustrating the figures given for each year.

Show your workings.

Activity 4

The management of an industrial company is considering methods of supplying financial information to its employees, many of whom are unfamiliar with financial matters. It is considered that a visual display in chart form, accompanied by oral explanations, is the best method of communication.

The following information for the five years from 19X1 to 19X5 inclusive is available:

Year	19X5 £m	19X4 £m	19X3 £m	19X2 £m	19X1 £m
Sales	6.3	6.5	5.8	4.7	3.9
Direct materials	3.1	3.2	2.8	2.2	1.9
Direct wages	1.4	1.2	1.1	1.0	0.8
Production overhead	1.0	1.0	0.9	0.8	0.6
Other overhead	0.4	0.4	0.3	0.2	0.2
Taxation	0.3	0.3	0.3	0.2	0.2
Profit	0.1	0.4	0.4	0.3	0.2

Product groups: %of total sales	%	%	%	%	%
Product A	24	22	20	20	15
B	12	10	11	9	12
C	16	21	23	26	30
Other products	48	47	46	45	43
	100	100	100	100	100

Tasks

(a)   As management accountant, prepare for the managing director a suitable bar chart (supported by any necessary calculation) to show sales by product groups.

(b)   Using the data given in (a), prepare a visual display of costs, taxation and profit for 19X4 and 19X5 with particular emphasis on direct wages. Use a different type of chart to that used in (a). Comment on your findings.

CHAPTER 4

QUESTIONS

GRAPHICAL PRESENTATION

Activity 1

The following table shows the monthly sales (in £'000) of Zabra Ltd for 19X4 and 19X5.

Month	Jan	Feb	March	April	May	June
19X4	20	20	25	18	16	25
19X5	18	21	26	16	20	26

Month	July	Aug	Sept	Oct	Nov	Dec
19X4	18	17	19	18	19	26
19X5	24	28	28	32	33	41

Task

Draw a Z chart from this information for 19X5.

Activity 2

The AT Photographic Company's sales of its Space Age camera for the two years 19X8/19X9 and 19X9/19Y0 were as follows:

	19X8/19X9	19X9/19Y0
June	562	705
July	514	624
August	648	582
September	566	711
October	743	862
November	816	1,027
December	863	963
January	627	706
February	428	531
March	558	664
April	564	713
May	811	912

Task

Round each month's sales to the nearest hundred and use this data to prepare a Z chart for 19X9/19Y0.

Activity 3

The following table shows the number of orders received by a firm during October 19X6, analysed according to their value ranges and sales values:

Value range	Number of orders	Sales value of orders £
Under £50	322	10,800
£50, under £100	245	18,000
£100, under £500	77	18,000
£500, under £1,000	35	30,000
£1,000, under £2,500	21	43,200

Task

Draw a Lorenz curve from this data.

Activity 4

The following figures show incomes before tax and benefits, and after tax and benefits, of sections of the population.

Population m	Income before tax and benefits £m	Income after tax and benefits £m
10	6.25	9.375
10	6.25	9.375
10	12.50	18.750
5	25.00	18.750
5	50.00	18.750
40m	£100.00m	£75.00m

Tasks

(a)   Draw two Lorenz curves, ie before tax and benefits, and after tax and benefits. Show tabular working.

(b)   Comment briefly on these curves.

Activity 5

In preparing a report on advertising costs for a proposed new newspaper, the following information was collated about newspapers already in circulation:

Newspaper	Circulation (millions)	Advertising rate per page (£'000)
A	4.08	21.9
B	3.49	21.3
C	2.00	14.7
D	1.86	14.5
E	1.63	8.6
F	0.77	6.3
G	0.49	6.0

Tasks

(a)   Plot the data on a scatter graph.

(b)   Fit, by eye, a straight line to the points.

(c)   Use the line to estimate a suitable advertising rate for the new newspaper which is expected to have a circulation of one million.

Activity 6

The times taken (in minutes) by 35 employees in a factory to complete an operation are as follows:

5.6	6.9	4.3	6.8	6.3
8.9	3.1	5.6	7.3	8.4
4.6	4.1	3.8	6.2	7.5
3.8	2.1	4.7	5.6	6.1
5.4	6.2	5.1	5.6	7.5
5.7	2.8	5.4	9.0	5.1
8.3	7.9	5.8	4.2	1.7

Tasks

(a)   Present the data in the form of a grouped frequency table.

(b)   Present the data in the form of a histogram.

(c)   Plot a 'less than' cumulative frequency curve and from it obtain the median time (ie, the time corresponding to half the total frequency).

Activity 7

Task

Answer all of the following questions:

(a)   Compare and contrast the diagrammatic features of bar charts and histograms, and clearly differentiate their purposes. You may use sketches to supplement your answer.

(b)   Compare and contrast the meanings and uses of the mean, the mode and the median.

(c)   A new index number is to be created for future use. Explain the five main characteristics of an index number that will have to be considered.

Activity 8

Two competing fast-food companies, A and B, each operate a chain of restaurants in the same towns around the country. For one particular recent week, data for both companies was as follows:

Number of customers per week	Number of restaurants A	B	Total weekly turnover A £	B £
150, under 200	7	3	1,620	6,800
200, under 250	62	11	21,640	19,380
250, under 300	34	58	35,690	109,140
300, under 500	19	84	58,950	147,560
500, under 1,000	3	24	43,600	57,120

Tasks

(a)   Estimate the total number of customers in each class who visited each company's restaurants.

(b)   Calculate and draw *two* Lorenz curves, on the same graph, showing the relationships between proportions of total customers and total turnover for both companies.

(c)   What information do the two curves provide?

Activity 9

The following data describes the length of time, in minutes, taken by 60 employees in the accounts section of P Ltd using photocopier X during the course of a typical working day:

1.2	10.1	7.3	3.1	8.4	3.7	1.4	6.6	5.1	6.0
5.7	0.5	6.2	2.4	4.5	4.8	2.7	4.9	9.2	6.2
4.3	11.4	6.5	5.0	3.9	9.0	11.6	5.7	10.9	7.4
1.9	8.6	9.1	1.9	5.1	6.3	3.9	7.0	8.6	5.7
3.4	7.2	0.8	6.8	7.6	6.9	4.8	8.9	4.9	5.3
2.9	1.6	3.4	10.7	6.0	7.4	5.2	4.5	5.8	8.1

Tasks

(a)   Form these data into a frequency distribution of six classes and comment upon its shape.
(b)   Draw, on graph paper, the histogram of this frequency distribution.
(c)   Use the histogram to estimate the mode. Explain your result clearly.
(d)   Calculate the mean of the frequency distribution.

CHAPTER 5

QUESTIONS

TIME SERIES ANALYSIS

Activity 1

A domestic appliance retailer offers customers the chance to purchase an insurance policy to cover the cost of repairs, if needed, over five years. The policy can only be purchased when the appliance is first purchased.

The following table shows the sales of appliances, together with the number of policies sold, over the period 19X1 to 19X7.

Year	Sales of appliances at 19X1 prices (£'000)	Sales of policies (number)
19X1	3,000	400
19X2	5,000	300
19X3	7,000	600
19X4	10,000	1,200
19X5	15,000	1,700
19X6	18,000	2,200
19X7	19,000	2,000

Tasks

(a)   Plot a scatter graph of sales of appliances against year and draw by eye the line of best fit.

(b)   By extrapolating the line, forecast appliance sales for 19X8 and 19X9.

(c)   Plot a scatter graph of policy sales against appliance sales and draw the line of best fit.

(d)   Use the line obtained in (c) and the forecast of sales in (b) to predict policy sales for 19X8 and 19X9. Comment on the reliability of your forecast.

Activity 2

State which type of time series component you would expect to be prominent in the following types of data:

(a)   Monthly sales of ice cream by a long established ice cream vendor.

(b)   Monthly sales of bread by a new bakery steadily increasing its market share.

(c)   Quarterly sales of wellington boots by a long established manufacturer.

(d)   Annual passenger miles by an airline.

(e)   Sales of a staple product subject to obsolescence.

(f)   Volume of production per month from a factory where morale among the workforce is low, leading to frequent disputes, absenteeism and accidents.

Activity 3

The following are the sales figures for Bloggs Brothers Engineering Ltd for the 14 years from 19X1 to 19Y4:

Year	Sales £'000
19X1	491
19X2	519
19X3	407
19X4	452
19X5	607
19X6	681
19X7	764
19X8	696
19X9	751
19Y0	802
19Y1	970
19Y2	1,026
19Y3	903
19Y4	998

Task

Using the method of moving averages, establish the general trend of sales.

Activity 4

The daily output of Malcan plc over a four week period is shown in the table below:

	Monday	Tuesday	Number of units of output Wednesday	Thursday	Friday
Week 1	187	203	208	207	217
Week 2	207	208	210	206	212
Week 3	202	210	212	205	214
Week 4	208	215	217	217	213

Tasks

(a) Establish the five-period moving average trend of output.
(b) Display on a graph the actual data together with the trend figures.

Activity 5

The following table gives the takings (£'000) of a shopkeeper in each quarter of four successive years:

Quarter	1	2	3	4
19X1	13	22	58	23
19X2	16	28	61	25
19X3	17	29	61	26
19X4	18	30	65	29

Task

Calculate the trend figures and draw a graph to show the overall trend and the original data.

Activity 6

Live births in England and Wales:

Year	Quarter 1 ('000)	Quarter 2 ('000)	Quarter 3 ('000)	Quarter 4 ('000)
1	162	163	164	150
2	155	156	153	140
3	151	150	147	137

Task

By means of a moving average, find the trend and seasonal adjustments.

CHAPTER 6

QUESTIONS

INDEX NUMBERS

Activity 1

Task

Given the following prices and sale quantities for a model of refrigerator sold by an electrical wholesaler, calculate price and quantity relatives for 19X2 and 19X3 with 19X1 as base. Comment on the results.

Sales of Model A refrigerator, 19X1 to 19X3

Year	Price £	Sales '000
19X1	120	5.3
19X2	125	5.2
19X3	131	5.0

Activity 2

Task

Calculate the Laspeyre and Paasche price indices for the following data, using 19X4 as base year:

Item	19X4		19X5	
	Price (p_0)	Quantity (q_0)	Price (p_1)	Quantity (q_1)
Milk	19p a pint	50,000 pints	26p a pint	70,000 pints
Bread	39p a loaf	30,000 loaves	40p a loaf	40,000 loaves
Soap	42p a pack	20,000 packs	64p a pack	25,000 packs
Sugar	60p a kilo	10,000 kilos	68p a kilo	8,000 kilos
Eggs	84p a box	3,000 boxes	72p a box	2,500 boxes

Activity 3

A survey of four companies which make similar products produced the following data on the price (p) of the products and the quantity (q) sold in three separate years.

	Year 1		Year 2		Year 3	
	p	q	p	q	p	q
Company A	2	6	3	7	3	10
Company B	4	2	4	7	5	8
Company C	4	12	6	3	5	9
Company D	8	9	7	14	9	4

Task

Produce a base weighted (Laspeyre) aggregative quantity index for years 2 and 3 using year 1 as base.

Activity 4

A shopkeeper received the following amounts from the sale of radios:

19X1	£1,000
19X2	£1,100
19X3	£1,210
19X4	£1,331
19X5	£1,464

Task

Is it correct to say that the annual rate of increase of sales of radios is getting larger?

Activity 5

Set out below is the annual average general index of retail prices for each of the years 19X4 to 19Y5:

Year	Index
19X4	108.5
19X5	134.8
19X6	157.1
19X7	182.0
19X8	197.1
19X9	223.5
19Y0	263.7
19Y1	295.0
19Y2	320.4
19Y3	335.1
19Y4	351.8
19Y5	373.2

Task

Re-state the index numbers for the 12 years using the chain index basis.

Activity 6

Task

Construct an index number for four commodities A, B, C and D with prices 110, 98, 136 and 125 respectively:

(a)   using weights 10, 5, 3 and 2 respectively; and
(b)   using weights 90, 5, 3 and 2 respectively.

Activity 7

Task

Compare the following two sets of index numbers which relate to the sales of *Biffo* and *Woof-Woof* dog foods.

	19X2	*19X3*	*19X4*	*19X5*	*19X6*
Biffo	61	88	100	135	165
Woof-Woof	210	230	250	300	360

Activity 8

Set out below is the annual average general index of retail prices for each of the years 19X4 to 19Y5:

Year	*Index*
19X4	108.5
19X5	134.8
19X6	157.1
19X7	182.0
19X8	197.1
19X9	223.5
19Y0	263.7
19Y1	295.0
19Y2	320.4
19Y3	335.1
19Y4	351.8
19Y5	373.2

Task

Re-state the index numbers for each of the 12 years using 19Y0 as the base year equal to 100.

Activity 9

Task

Taking 19X0 as the base year, calculate index numbers for prices and quantities for each of the items separately for year 19X1 for the following data and comment on the results.

Item	19X0		19X1	
	Price (£)	*Quantity*	*Price (£)*	*Quantity*
A	0.20	20	0.22	24
B	0.25	12	0.28	16
C	1.00	3	0.98	2

Activity 10

The following data, which was taken from the *New Earnings Survey* for 19X5 and 19X7, shows the number of men and women included in the surveys who were employed in administrative and clerical work, together with the corresponding wages.

Occupational category	Sex	19X5		19X7	
		Numbers ('000)	Wages	Numbers ('000)	Wages
Administrative	Female	14	195	17	238
	Male	62	270	70	328
Clerical	Female	165	118	174	137
	Male	76	159	77	181

Tasks

(a)   For each of the following calculate a base weighted index number which shows the increase in wages:

(i)   all employees;
(ii)   male employees;
(iii) administrative employees.

(b)   The corresponding index numbers for female employees and clerical employees are 116.8 and 115.2 respectively. Write a report commenting on the data and your findings.

Activity 11

The following information has been collected for 'Noddyland':

	Weights	Indexes for 19X8 (Jan 19X2 as base)
Food	299	123
Alcoholic drink	72	127
Tobacco	76	125
Fuel and light	71	134
Durable household goods	67	113
Clothing and footwear	102	113
Transport	136	119
Miscellaneous goods	68	125
Services	63	132
Meals bought and consumed outside home	46	127

Task

Using this information, calculate an index of retail prices for 'Noddyland'.

Activity 12

Printed below is a summary of the Official Statistics relating to output of the production industries for the first quarter of year 19X5:

	Industry	Weight	Index average 19X0 = 100
	Energy and water supply		
A	Coal and coke	41	35.6
B	Extraction of mineral oil and natural gas	123	154.7
C	Mineral oil processing	15	99.3
D	Other energy and water supply	85	98.6
	Manufacturing industries		
E	Metals	25	108.0
F	Other minerals and mineral products	41	92.1
G	Chemicals and man-made fibres	68	118.9
H	Engineering and allied industries	325	101.2
I	Food, drink and tobacco	99	101.3
J	Textiles, footwear, clothing and leather	52	97.9
K	Paper, printing and publishing	68	95.6
L	All other manufacturing	58	94.1

(Central Statistical Office)

Tasks

(a)   Calculate an index number for all production industries combined ie, those referenced A to L.

(b)   Calculate an index number for the industries concerned with energy and water ie, those referenced A to D.

CHAPTER 7

QUESTIONS

MAIN TYPES OF
PERFORMANCE INDICATORS

Activity 1

You are presented with the following summarised information concerning J Free:

Trading, profit and loss account (extracts) for the year to 30 April 19X2 and 30 April 19X3

	19X3 £	19X2 £
Sales (all on credit)	200,000	120,000
Cost of sales	(150,000)	(80,000)
Gross profit	50,000	40,000
Expenses	(15,000)	(10,000)
Net profit	35,000	30,000

Balance sheet (extracts) at 30 April 19X2 and 30 April 19X3

	19X3 £	19X3 £	19X2 £	19X2 £
Fixed assets (net book value)		12,000		15,000
Current assets				
Stocks	18,000		7,000	
Trade debtors	36,000		12,000	
Cash at bank	–		1,000	
		54,000		20,000
		66,000		35,000
Capital account				
Balance at 1 April	29,000		12,000	
Net profit for the year	35,000		30,000	
	64,000		42,000	
Less: Drawings	(23,000)		(13,000)	
		41,000		29,000
Current liabilities				
Trade creditors	15,000		6,000	
Bank overdraft	10,000		–	
		25,000		6,000
		66,000		35,000

Notes

(1)   There were no purchases or disposals of fixed assets during the year.

(2)   During 19X2/19X3 Free reduced his selling prices in order to stimulate sales.

(3)   It may be assumed that price levels were stable.

Tasks

(a)   Calculate the following ratios for both 19X2 and 19X3:

      (i)   net profit on sales;
      (ii)   gross profit on sales;
      (iii)   return on capital employed;
      (iv)   debtor collection period;
      (v)   current ratio; and
      (vi)   acid test (or quick) ratio.

(b)   State what changes appear to have arisen as a result of the reduction in selling prices.

Activity 2

The following extracts relate to K George's accounts for the year to 31 August 19X4:

Trading, profit and loss account for the year to 31 August 19X4

	£	£
Sales (all credit)		100,000
Less: Cost of goods sold		
Opening stock	10,000	
Purchases	52,000	
	62,000	
Less: Closing stock	(12,000)	
		(50,000)
Gross profit		50,000
Less: Expenses		(25,000)
Net profit		25,000

Balance sheet at 31 August 19X4

		£	£
Fixed assets			
	Machinery at cost	30,000	
	Less: Depreciation	(12,000)	
			18,000
Current assets			
	Stocks	12,000	
	Trade debtors	7,000	
	Bank	1,000	
			20,000
Less: Current liabilities			
	Trade creditors	5,000	
			(5,000)
			33,000
Financed by			
	Capital		18,000
	Net profit for the year		25,000
	Less: Drawings		(10,000)
			33,000

Tasks

Calculate the following accounting ratios:

(a)   gross profit percentage;
(b)   net profit percentage;
(c)   return on capital employed;
(d)   stock turnover;
(e)   debtor collection period;
(f)   current ratio; and
(g)   quick (or acid test).

Activity 3

A company wishes to measure the efficiency of its machine operators. It has a special order for a variation on the normal type of product it produces of 50,000 units in the next three months. It estimates that machinists should spend one hour to produce one unit.

49,000 units were produced within the available period and total machinists' time totalled 47,500 hours.

Task

What can be said about the economy, effectiveness and efficiency of the machine operators?

Activity 4

Total rail business	British Rail	19X6/X7	19X7/X8	19X8/X9	19X9/Y0	19Y0/Y1
41 Total receipts per train mile	£	9.48	9.52	9.47	10.72	10.25
42 Total operating expenses per train mile	£	12.85	12.58	11.54	13.36	13.28
43 Train miles per member of staff (total staff productivity)	miles	1,812	1,967	2,123	2,113	2,114
44 Revenue per £1,000 gross paybill costs	£	1,510	1,594	1,711	1,615	1,574
45 Train miles per train crew member (train crew productivity)	miles	8,564	9,568	10,485	10,727	10,961
46 Train miles per single track mile	'000	12.6	13.1	13.5	13.5	13.7

The above information has come from the accounts of British Rail.

Some of the indicators are partly based on financial data (41, 42 and 44). These have been adjusted to take account of changing price levels by converting each to 19Y0/Y1 price levels using the GDP deflator.

Task

For each of the performance indicators, briefly give your opinion on the success or otherwise of British Rail over the five-year period.

Activity 5

The following information is provided for a 30-day period for the rooms department of a hotel:

	Rooms with twin beds	Single rooms
Number of rooms in hotel	260	70
Number of rooms available to let	240	40
Average number of rooms occupied daily	200	30

Number of guests in period	6,450
Average length of stay	2 days
Total revenue in period	£774,000
Number of employees	200
Payroll costs for period	£100,000
Items laundered in period	15,000
Cost of cleaning supplies in period	£5,000
Total cost of laundering	£22,500
Listed daily rate for twin-bedded room	£110
Listed daily rate for single room	£70

The hotel calculates a number of statistics, including the following:

Room occupancy	Total number of rooms occupied as a percentage of rooms available to let
Bed occupancy	Total number of beds occupied as a percentage of beds available
Average guest rate	Total revenue divided by number of guests
Revenue utilisation	Actual revenue as a percentage of maximum revenue from available rooms
Average cost per occupied bed	Total cost divided by number of beds occupied

Task

Prepare a table which contains the following statistics, calculated to one decimal place:

(a)   room occupancy (%)
(b)   bed occupancy (%)
(c)   average guest rate (£)
(d)   revenue utilisation (%)
(e)   cost of cleaning supplies per occupied room per day (£)
(f)   average cost per occupied bed per day (£)

CHAPTER 8

QUESTIONS

WRITING REPORTS

Activity 1

Task

You have been asked to write a report on the wages in the car manufacturing industry. State *three* published statistical series that would be useful to your report, giving reasons for your choice and stating where the information might be found.

Activity 2

'A report can be presented efficiently by using headings and sub-headings as a feature of layout.'

Task

Name the headings that are typically used to introduce the main sections of a specially commissioned report.

Activity 3

Your busy superior at the Children's Educational Welfare Protection Society (within which you are an appointed personal deputy) requires a report from you concerning the procedure adopted by the Education Authority for selecting pupils for college scholarships. He wants it to be simple because he says he 'has no time for red tape'. All you have is a copiously-written draft 'letter for parents' given to you by a colleague who has researched this.

Task

Provide the required report from this letter, which is given below.

Following the written examination taken by candidates on 3 February, *some* children have now been selected by the Education Committee for scholarships to college commencing in the autumn term of this year. The parents of those children have been informed of this. In the case of all other candidates, of whom your child is one, a final decision has not yet been made.

The next stage in the selection procedure will be the investigation of the cases of those candidates on the borderline for scholarships. You must not, however, assume that your child will necessarily be one of these children. Indeed, in the case of the majority of parents who receive notification of procedure, their children will not be among the borderline group.

The investigation of borderline cases will be carried out by a number of panels specially appointed by the Education Committee for this particular purpose. These panels will visit schools concerned to discuss each borderline case with the Head, to examine the schoolwork that the children have been doing and then to interview them. This stage in the selection procedure will commence in March and will not be completed until, at the earliest, the end of June.

Within about two weeks following the visit to a school by an interviewing panel, letters will be sent to the Head of the school for transmission to the parents of all candidates apart from those already selected following the February examination. In the letter which you will receive you will either be informed that your child has not been selected for a scholarship and that he/she will not be considered further under the entrance examination selection procedure, or you will be told that your child has been interviewed and is still under consideration and that the final decision concerning him/her will be made towards the end of June. In the latter case, there will be enclosed a copy of the form B81, which the parent will be asked to complete and return through the Head of his child's school (except in the case of candidates attending schools not maintained by the County Council, where the parent will already have completed one of these). If you receive this type of letter, there will also be mentioned in it that a further communication will be sent to you towards the end of July, informing you whether or not your child has been selected for a scholarship. If he/she is selected, you will at the same time be told the name of the college where a place is offered.

It is fully appreciated that the parent of a child who has been interviewed will have to wait for a period before he receives the final letter telling him what has been decided concerning his child. This, however, is unavoidable due to the time that is required for a thorough investigation of all borderline cases.

CHAPTER 9

QUESTIONS

ORGANISATIONS - STRUCTURE AND PERFORMANCE

Activity 1

Explain briefly the different ways in which organisations may be classified.

Activity 2

Explain the principles of specific order costing.

Activity 3

Explain the different cost classifications which may be used.

Activity 4

Distinguish between quantitative and qualitative performance measures.

CHAPTER 10

QUESTIONS

REPORTING

Activity 1

Distinguish the information needs of strategic, tactical and operational management.

Activity 2

What are the characteristics of good information?

Activity 3

Give examples of regulatory reporting.

QUESTIONS

UNIT 8

PREPARING VAT RETURNS

CHAPTER 1

QUESTIONS

INTRODUCTION TO VAT - SUPPLIES AND REGISTRATION

1   Activity

Calculate the VAT on the following net prices:

(a)   £216.00;
(b)   £5,926.00;
(c)   £11,144.00.

2   Activity

Calculate the VAT on the following gross prices:

(a)   £715.81.
(b)   £1,292.50.
(c)   £7,336.23.

3   Activity

Su Chin makes violins, violas and cellos. In order to do so she has to buy, amongst other items, wood. She has bought wood for one cello costing £1,000 on which she pays VAT at 17.5%. When she has produced the cello from this wood then she will sell it to a musical instrument dealer, Jake, for £3,000 plus VAT at 17.5% and he will sell it to a customer, the consumer, for £6,000 plus VAT at 17.5%.

How much VAT is paid to Customs & Excise by Su Chin and by Jake, and how much will the consumer pay for the cello?

4   Activity

A trader buys goods for £1,762.50 including VAT at 17.5% and sells them for £2,000 plus VAT at 17.5%. How much VAT is paid to Customs & Excise?

5   Activity

Which of the following supplies are exempt and which are taxable?

(a)   Mortgage advisory services.
(b)   Clothes retailing.
(c)   Trade union subscriptions.
(d)   Repairs to domestic appliances.
(e)   Interior design.
(f)   Eye test fees.
(g)   Cremations.
(h)   Repairs to cars.
(i)   Courier delivery services.

6   Activity

Which types of supply are the following items?

(a)   Adult clothes.
(b)   Children's clothes.
(c)   Food from a Chinese takeaway.
(d)   Chocolate bars.
(e)   School fees.
(f)   Holiday lettings.
(g)   New houses.
(h)   New office buildings.
(i)   Bouquets.

7   Activity

What are the VAT consequences of making the following supplies?

(a)   A gift costing £5 to a customer.

(b)   A gift of a gold watch costing £280 to a member of staff as a long service award.

(c)   A sample of soap powder to every household in a district of London.

(d)   A meal pack consisting of a sandwich, packet of crisps and a chocolate bar.

(e)   A 'coffee table' book, with a leather bookmark.

8   Activity

Interpretations Ltd sells gift sets. Some of the sets consist of a set of compact discs together with a book about the work and the composer. Others simply comprise the book, supplied in a presentation case.

The VAT exclusive selling price of the book and discs is £75, and of the book alone, £50. The cost of producing the books is £10, the cost of producing the discs is £8, and the presentation case for the book alone cost £1 to produce.

What VAT should be charged on the supply?

9   Activity

Which of the following could be taxable persons, and in respect of which businesses?

(a)   Jones, a carpenter, who collects stamps as a hobby.

(b)   Mary and Jane, who are in partnership together providing catering services. Jane also runs a part time hairdressing business.

(c)   Donald and Douglas are in business together as photographers. They also run an antique shop. Donald and his wife Dora have a guest house. Dora also has a beauty salon.

(d)   Slick Slacks Ltd, a clothing shop. The company is owned by Sally Steel, who also runs a business as an interior design consultant.

CHAPTER 2

QUESTIONS

VAT INVOICES, VAT PERIODS, RECORDS REQUIRED

1   Activity

Consider the following invoice and comment upon whether or not it is a valid and correct tax invoice.

XYZ Ltd
123 Mount Place
London

To: ABC Ltd
789 St Johns Walk
Birmingham

23 July 1996

	£
Goods	2,160.00
VAT @ 17.5%	378.00
	2,538.00

Terms: 2% 30 days
3% 10 days
Net 60 days

2   Activity

Consider the following invoice and comment upon whether or not it is a valid and correct tax invoice.

All-u-want Ltd
2 High Street
Smallton
SL1 1LM

VAT No. 789 1234 56

Total   £82.99

(inclusive of VAT at the rate of ....%).

3   Activity

A trader sells various articles for the following net amounts. What is the VAT on each article?

(a)   £200
(b)   £480
(c)   £1,300
(d)   £2,360
(e)   £4,444
(f)   £8,080

4   Activity

A trader sells various articles for the following net amounts. What is the VAT on each article?

(a)   £580
(b)   £900
(c)   £1,280
(d)   £4,140
(e)   £6,680
(f)   £9,120

5   Activity

A trader sells various articles for the following gross amounts. What is the VAT on each article?

(a)   £117.03
(b)   £991.70
(c)   £1,238.45
(d)   £4,761.57
(e)   £7,153.87
(f)   £9,973.40

6   Activity

A trader sells 25 size 1 widgets for £1.17 each, and 35 size 2 widgets for £1.59 each.

Calculate the VAT under each of the rounding rules.

7   Activity

Goods are to be sold for £1,000 plus VAT at 17.5%. The terms of the sale are that a 3% cash discount is offered for payment within 10 days and a 2% discount for payment within 21 days.

What amounts would appear on the invoice for the sale of the goods and the VAT?

8   Activity

Calculate the VAT that would be charged on the following sale:

No	Item	Unit price £
5	Crates	10.05
8	Tubs	13.25
6	Barrels	15.15

A 5% cash discount is offered for settlement within 7 days.

9   Activity

Giles has been allocated prescribed accounting periods ending 28 February, 31 May, 31 August and 30 November.

What action should he take if:

(a)   He changes his accounting date to 5 April.
(b)   He expands his business abroad so that he will be due repayments of VAT.

10   Activity

John's financial year ends on 31 December 1997; his annual turnover is less than £100,000. He uses the annual accounting scheme and had made three quarterly payments of £720 each. In the event his liability is £3,820.

What return and payments must he make for the year, and what payments must he make for the following year?

11   Activity

Larry, a trader, keeps the following records:

(a)   A copy of the tax invoices he issues.

(b)   A list of the tax invoices in the order in which they are paid by the customer, showing the VAT and the VAT inclusive amount.

(c)   The tax invoices he receives (in no particular order).

(d)   A list of the purchase invoices in the order he pays them, showing the VAT and the VAT inclusive amount.

The VAT account in the nominal ledger (ie, part of Larry's bookkeeping system) is completed by his accountant once a year. Larry makes no imports or exports.

Are Larry's records adequate?

CHAPTER 3

QUESTIONS

COMPLETING THE VAT RETURN

1 Activity

Michael had issued the following tax invoices:

Invoice No	Gross £	VAT £	Net £
001	2,300	300	2,000
002	2,400	400	2,000

What should he do?

2 Activity

The following details were extracted from Stella's books for the 3 months to 31 May 1996.

Purchases Day Book

	Description	Gross £	VAT £	Purchases £	Expenses £
Mar	Total	21,150	3,150	16,000	2,000
Apr	Total	19,975	2,975	14,000	3,000
May	Total	18,800	2,800	14,000	2,000

Sales day book

	Description	Gross £	VAT £	Sales £	Other £
Mar	Total	27,025	4,025	23,000	
Apr	Total	24,675	3,675	21,000	
May	Total	28,200	4,200	22,000	2,000

Note: office furniture was sold for £2,000 plus VAT in May.

Cash payments book

	Description	Gross £	VAT £	Purchases £	Wages £	Creditors £
Mar	Total	26,380	280	1,600	12,000	12,500
Apr	Total	28,320	420	2,400	12,500	13,000
May	Total	27,850	350	2,000	11,500	14,000

Cash receipts book

	Description	Gross £	VAT £	Sales £	Debtors £
Mar	Total	22,850	350	2,000	20,500
Apr	Total	23,175	175	1,000	22,000
May	Total	23,350	350	2,000	21,000

Compute her outputs and output tax, and her inputs and input tax.

3   Activity

A trader provides the following information for his VAT quarter ended 31 July 1996.

He has made 5 sales, each standard rated, for net amounts of £2,000, £3,600, £4,000, £6,000 and £10,000. In each case he allowed a cash discount of 5%.

He has made various purchases. He has a bundle of less detailed invoices totalling £1,880 in which VAT was included at the rate of 17.5%. In addition he has one invoice from a major supplier for £11,750 (including VAT).

He has paid wages of £6,000, and received insurance proceeds of £5,200 following fire damage.

Show the entries that would appear on the VAT return for the three months to 31 July 1996.

	Value Added Tax Return	For Official Use
	For the period	

HM Customs and Excise

Registration number

Period

You could be liable to a financial penalty if your completed return and all the VAT payable are not received by the due date.

Due date:

For Official Use	

Your VAT Office telehpone number is

ATTENTION

If you are using Retail Scheme B1, D or J, please remember to carry out your annual adjustment at the appropriate time.

Before you fill in this form please read the notes on the back and the VAT leaflet 'Filling in your VAT return'. Fill in all boxes clearly in ink, and write 'none' where necessary. Don't put a dash or leave any box blank. If there are no pence write "00" in the pence column. Do not enter more than one amount in any box.

For official use			
	VAT due in this period on sales and other outputs	1	
	VAT due in this period on acquisitions from other EC Member States	2	
	Total VAT due (the sum of boxes 1 and 2)	3	
	VAT reclaimed in this period on purchases and other inputs (including acquisitions from the EC)	4	
	Net VAT to be paid to Customs or reclaimed by you (Difference between boxes 3 and 4)	5	
	Total value of sales and all other outputs excluding any VAT, include your box 8 figure	6	00
	Total value of purchases and all other inputs excluding any VAT, include your box 9 figure	7	00
	Total value of all supplies of goods and related services, excluding any VAT, to other EC Member States	8	00
	Total value of all acquisitions of goods and related services, excluding any VAT, from other EC Member States	9	00

Retail schemes.   If you have used any of the schemes in the period covered by this return, enter the relevant letter(s) in this box.

If you are enclosing a payment please tick this box.	DECLARATION: You, or someone on your behalf, must sign below.
	I _ __ ___ ___ ___ __ ___ __ ___ __ ___ ___ _ declare that the
	(Full name of signatory in BLOCK LETTERS)
	information given above is true and complete.
	Signature _ __ ___ ___ __ ___ ___ _Date _ _____ _19 _ __ _

A false declaration can result in prosecution.

CD 2859/N3(08/93)   F3790 (February 1994)

VAT 100

CHAPTER 4

QUESTIONS

SPECIAL CASES

1   Activity

James has been using the cash accounting scheme for many years. All sales and purchases are made by cheque. He provides the following lists of invoices issued and received for the quarter ended 31 August 1996:

(a)   Sales invoices

Date	Gross £	VAT £	Net £	Paid
25.5.96	1,645	245	1,400	3.6.96
10.6.96	1,175	175	1,000	21.6.96
25.6.96	2,350	350	2,000	11.7.96
7.7.96	1,880	280	1,600	23.8.96
28.7.96	2,115	315	1,800	3.9.96
16.8.96	2,585	385	2,200	29.8.96
24.8.96	1,410	210	1,200	15.9.96

(b)   Purchase invoices

Date	Gross £	VAT £	Net £	Paid
25.5.96	705	105	600	29.6.96
9.6.96	940	140	800	29.6.96
29.6.96	1,175	175	1,000	30.7.96
16.7.96	3,525	525	3,000	30.7.96
3.8.96	705	105	600	29.8.96
24.8.96	470	70	400	28.9.96

What are the details of outputs and output tax, and inputs and input tax to be entered on James' VAT return for the quarter to 31 August 1996?

2   Activity

R Jones & Co Ltd made the following sales to Caroline:

Date	Type of supply	Gross £
1.1.97	Standard rated	4,700
21.1.97	Zero rated	5,000
12.2.97	Standard rated	2,350
11.3.97	Standard rated	3,525

On 24 April 1997 Caroline paid £6,700 on account. A month later she was declared bankrupt, and R Jones & Co Ltd wrote off the remaining debt.

All the VAT had been accounted for on the return for the quarter ended 31 March 1997.

How much bad debt relief can be claimed and when?

3   Activity

A VAT registered trader buys a car for use in the business at a cost of £24,000 plus VAT. At the time of the purchase he has a compact disc player installed at a cost of £470 including VAT. Two months later a mobile telephone is installed in the car solely for business use and the invoiced cost of this is £235 including VAT. The car is used 5% for private purposes.

How much of the VAT relating to the car is recoverable and at what amount will the car be included in the accounts of the business?

CHAPTER 5

QUESTIONS

ADMINISTRATION

1   Activity

Jack has been asked by one of his UK customers to send some goods to him through the post. Jack will make a separate charge for postage and packing. The goods themselves are zero rated. Should he charge VAT?

Use the VAT Guide to prepare your answer.

2   Activity

Robert and Richard have been trading in partnership, under the name R & R Services. They are registered for VAT.

They decide to admit Naomi into partnership on 1 February 1997, and to change the name to R 'N R Services. Must they notify HM Customs and Excise, and, if so, what is the time limit?

Use the VAT Guide to prepare your answer.

PRACTICE DEVOLVED

ASSESSMENTS

QUESTIONS

UNIT 7

PRACTICE DEVOLVED ASSESSMENT 1

QUESTIONS

EDWARDS ELECTRONICS LTD

Time allowed 3 hours

The profit and loss figures of Edwards Electronics Ltd for the past three years are as follows:

Financial year (to 31 December annually)	19X0 £'000	19X1 £'000	19X2 £'000
Sales revenue	403.2	423.0	442.8
Cost of sales	(216.6)	(235.0)	(242.3)
Gross profit	186.6	188.0	200.5
Other income	4.4	8.2	16.8
	191.0	196.2	217.3
General expenses			
Administrative expense	(129.4)	(132.4)	(131.2)
Sales and distribution costs	(43.7)	(42.8)	(44.6)
Interest costs	(6.8)	(7.0)	(12.2)
Net profit	11.1	14.0	29.3
Taxation	(3.9)	(5.3)	(11.7)
Profit after taxation	7.2	8.7	17.6
Dividends	(3.8)	(4.5)	(8.8)
Retained profits	3.4	4.2	8.8

The company finance director, Jeff Thompson, has been analysing the results and has produced the following additional detail of factors that have affected the company position over the three year period:

Financial performance affectors – 19X0–19X2

	19X0	19X1	19X2
Inflation indices (prices basically rising by 6% per annum)	112.0	118.72	125.84
Average interest rate over the financial year (as borne by Edwards Electronics Ltd)	18%	19%	12.5%

Balance sheet figures (to 31 December annually)

Financial year	*19X0* £'000	*19X1* £'000	*19X2* £'000
Fixed assets	180.2	189.7	197.6
Current assets			
Stocks	71.0	80.6	91.0
Debtors and prepayments	78.1	81.9	88.1
Bank and cash	42.0	37.2	32.0
Current liabilities			
Trade creditors	(96.2)	(80.8)	(63.2)
Other creditors and accruals	(22.2)	(18.1)	(19.8)
Bank loan (long-term)	(17.2)	(18.6)	(45.0)
Net total assets	235.7	271.9	280.7
Financed by			
Capital	188.0	220.0	220.0
Retained profits	47.7	51.9	60.7
	235.7	271.9	280.7

Further information

Stocks at beginning of 19X0 = £68,300

Annual purchases	219.3	244.6	252.7

Task 1

You have been asked by Jeff Thompson to analyse company condition and performance – initially by evaluating the condition and performance ratios suggested in the following pro-forma company analysis sheets:

Liquidity/Cashflow indicators			
Financial year	*19X0*	*19X1*	*19X2*
Current ratio: [Current assets: Current liabilities]			
Acid test ratio: [Current assets – Stocks: Current liabilities]			
Cash ratio: [Cash: Current liabilities]			

Performance indicators

Financial year	*19X0*	*19X1*	*19X2*

Return on capital employed (ROCE)
[Net profit/Owners investment × 100 (%)]

Net profit margin
[Net profit/Sales × 100 (%)]

Asset efficiency/Turnover
[Sales/Net total assets]

Gross profit margin
[Gross profit/Sales × 100 (%)]

Expense: Sales ratios
Admin. expenses: Sales
Distribution costs: Sales
Interest costs: Sales
[All measured as % figures]

Fixed asset efficiency/Turnover
[Sales/Fixed assets]

Stock turnover
[Cost of sales: Average stock]

Debtor turnover
[Sales: Debtors]

Debtor payment period
[Debtors/Sales × 365]

Creditor turnover
[Purchases: Creditors]

Creditor payment period
[Creditors/Purchases × 365]

Gearing indicators

Financial year	*19X0*	*19X1*	*19X2*

Gearing ratio:
    [Interest-bearing debt: Owners investment]

Leverage:
    [All creditor funding: Owners investment]

Interest cover:
    [Profits before interest: Interest incurred
    (per P/L)]

Task 2

Jeff Thompson has asked you to confirm his views on company performance over the three-year period. Make your responses in short (but *clear* and *full*) note form and support with the figures you calculated for task 1 or other calculations where possible. Jeff's views are expressed in the following notes:

The inflation indices given in my earlier note indicate an inflation rate of 6% annually over 19X1 and 19X2.

Comment

The sales position is not healthy. Sales revenues have been growing and sales prices have been increasing roughly in line with inflation rates. However, inflation-adjusted 19X2 and 19X3 sales revenue figures to 19X1 price levels indicate that sales volumes have been falling.

Comment

The improved company performance over the three year period is largely a product of highly-effective cost control as indicated by cost of sales: sales and expenses: sales ratios.

Comment

The balance sheet figures show outstanding debt liabilities at the end of each year. These figures are not reflective/representative of the average amount of debt outstanding over the whole of each respective year.

Using the figures for the average interest rate charged to us annually and our annual interest charges in the P/L (from the earlier statements), the average amounts of interest-bearing debt over each year have been £37,777, £36,842 and £97,600 respectively.

Comment

The proportion of company profits taken up by taxation has increased over the three-year period.

Comment

Overall total profits have improved over the three-year period and the shareholders have benefited from the improvement. The company is in a healthier state generally.

Comment

Task 3

Briefly (but clearly) express your views on the other main aspects of the corporate performance of Edwards Electronics Ltd over the past three years, based on the figures and ratios you have evaluated. Your view should be expressed, amongst other things, on ROCE, sales margins and asset turnover ['asset efficiency'] and the management of debtor, creditor and stock periods.

The following analysis of sales revenue figures over the period 19X0–19X2 has been provided by Jeff Thompson:

Financial year	*19X0* £'000	*19X1* £'000	*19X2* £'000
Sales revenue Breakdown:	403.2	423.0	442.8
3 months to 31 March	78.8	84.6	91.0
3 months to 30 June	107.2	116.4	119.6
3 months to 30 September	85.9	93.4	98.2
3 months to 31 December	131.3	128.6	134.0

Task 4

Jeff has requested that you work time series analysis on the quarterly figures to present underlying trends as well as seasonal effects, quarter by quarter, over the three-year period. A pro-forma appears below:

TIME SERIES ANALYSIS				
				Figures in £'000
Time periods *19X0*	*Quarterly figures*	*4-quarterly moving average figures [Gen. trend]*	*4-quarterly moving average figures [Centred trend]*	*Seasonal effects [per quarter]*
3 months to 31 March	78.8			
3 months to 30 June	107.2			
3 months to 30 September				
3 months to 31 December				
19X1				
3 months to 31 March				
3 months to 30 June				
3 months to 30 September				
3 months to 31 December				
19X2				
3 months to 31 March				
3 months to 30 June				
3 months to 30 September				
3 months to 31 December				

Task 5

A chart is required for management. The chart should show a graph line for (actual) sales figures quarter by quarter and a graph line for the centred moving average trend. Prepare the necessary chart on the following pro-forma:

Time series chart – Sales revenues

Period of analysis – Financial years 19X0 – 19X2

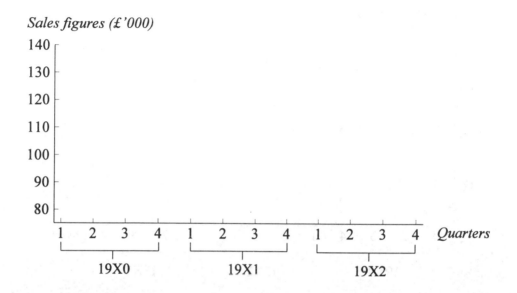

What is an average seasonal effect for a quarter ending on 30 September? Use your computations in task 4 to evaluate this.

Task 6

The management of Edwards Electronics Ltd requires a bar chart presentation of the quarterly sales results over the 19X0–19X2 period. The request is that you prepare multiple bar charts. Four bars (one representing each quarter) should be shown side by side for each year to represent the results for that year. The charts are required on the pro-forma below:

Sales revenues – Quarterly results

Period of analysis – Financial years 19X0 – 19X2

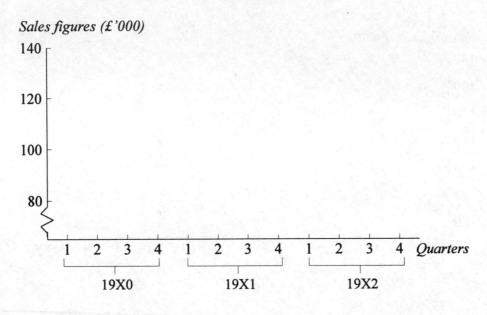

Task 7

The company also wants to display the sales results for 19X2 in the form of a pie chart; the pie chart should show the breakdown of total sales revenues for 19X2 into the proportions earned in each quarter. Prepare a suitable pie chart for the company:

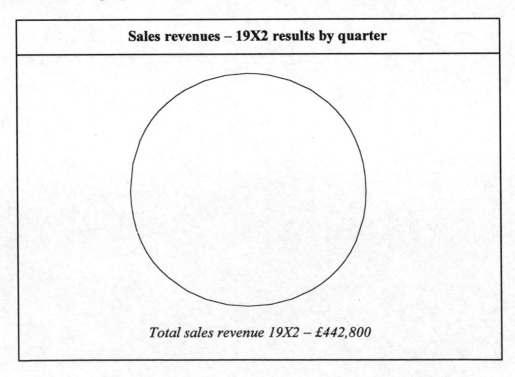

Total sales revenue 19X2 – £442,800

Task 8

As part of the analysis for financial year 19X2, Jeff Thompson has asked you to analyse results for production and sales of the Tristar TV, a relatively new company product. Computer printouts of budgets and results for the product over 19X2 are as follows:

Budgeted sales:	220		
Budgeted revenue:	£52,800	Budgeted unit cost:	£160
Actual sales:	190		
Actual revenue:	£46,550		
Budgeted production:	220		
Budgeted assembly time:	440 hours		
Actual production:	205		
Actual assembly time:	369 hours		

The analysis is to be made using the company pro-forma analysis sheets which follow. Complete the analysis sheets appropriately.

Edwards Electronics Ltd
Production evaluation

Product:

Period:

Production-Volume ratio:
(Actual output in standard hours as a percentage of budgeted hours)

Efficiency/Productivity ratio:
(Actual output in standard hours as a percentage of actual hours)

Capacity/Usage ratio:
(Actual hours as a percentage of budgeted hours)

Backing figures

Standard hour: *Units*
(Budgeted production over budgeted time)

Actual output in standard hours:

Actual hours worked:

Budgeted hours:

Edwards Electronics Ltd
Production evaluation

Product:

Period:

Budgeted sales revenue:

Budgeted cost of sales:

Budgeted gross profit margin:

Variances

Sales price variance:
[Actual unit sales × (actual SP – budget SP)]

Sales volume variance:
[Budgeted margin per unit × (actual unit sales – budgeted unit sales)]

[All figures to be shown in £s]

Task 9

Jeff Thompson has requested that you complete a return required by the Association of Electrical Contractors in respect of the financial year ending 31 December 19X2:

⬡ **A E C**   Association of Electrical Contractors
             18, Grafton Way, Herts, HA3 4PF

Annual performance results

ROCE
[% on owner's investment]   ☐   Debtor period   ☐

Gross margin on sales   ☐
                                              Creditor period   ☐
Net margin on sales   ☐
[using net profit before tax]

Asset turnover   ☐   Stock period   ☐
[Sales/Net total assets]

                                              [All periods in days]

Above figures taken from financial statements for the year to/as at . . . .

Results will be confidentially held and used only to produce general descriptive statistical information for the use of the Association and its members.

UNIT 7

PRACTICE DEVOLVED ASSESSMENT 2

QUESTIONS

MILLS CARPETS LTD

Time allowed 3 hours

Mills Carpets Ltd specialises in the production of woven wool Axminster and Wilton carpets.

Analysis of sales and prices for the last five years, together with the general index of retail prices (IRP) over the same period is given below.

Carpet production 19X1 to 19X5

			Year		
	19X1	*19X2*	*19X3*	*19X4*	*19X5*
Sales/Production ('000 sq yards)					
Axminster	10.2	10.8	11.3	11.8	12.3
Wilton	32.7	36.2	39.1	43.5	47.2
Selling price (£ per sq yard)					
Axminster	9.3	9.8	10.4	10.8	11.1
Wilton	12.3	13.1	13.8	14.9	15.6
IRP (1987 = 100)	201	211	222	230	237

(Year 19X5 is the last full accounting year)

Task 1

Suggest, with reasons, three other published statistical series that would assist in planning production for future years.

	Published statistic	*How it would be useful*
1		
2		
3		

Task 2

Calculate the total value of annual sales each year. Use the IRP to deflate these values to give the 'real terms' sales values at year 19X1 prices.

(Value = Price × Quantity)

$$\text{Deflated value at 19X1 prices} = \frac{\text{Actual value} \times \text{IRP for 19X1}}{\text{IRP for current year}}$$

	19X1	*19X2*	*19X3*	*19X4*	*19X5*
Total sales value (£'000)					
Value at 19X1 prices (£'000)					

Task 3

(a)   Calculate price index numbers for years 19X2 to 19X5 for each type of carpet separately.

(b)   As an aid to comparison with prices generally, calculate the IRP changing the base to year 19X1.

Index number calculations

Price index for year n = $\dfrac{P_n}{P_1} \times 100$

Change of base: Rebased index for year n = $\dfrac{\text{Old index for year n}}{\text{Old index for new base year}} \times 100$

Insert the results in the following pro-forma:

Price index number (19X1 = 100)

	19X1	*19X2*	*19X3*	*19X4*	*19X5*
Axminster					
Wilton					
IRP (19X1 = 100)					

Task 4

Plot graphs of sales volume per year of each type of carpet on the same axes with time on the horizontal axis. Use these to obtain extrapolated forecasts of production of each type of carpet for 19X6.

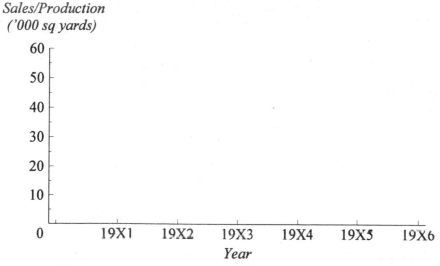

Forecasts for 19X6
Axminster production:
Wilton production:

Task 5

Write a memo to the sales director analysing sales and prices variations and trends over the period 19X1 to 19X5 and give a statistical forecast of sales volume for 19X6.

Task 6

Franklin plc is a competitor in the same industry and it has been operating for many years. You have obtained the following information relating to Franklin plc:

(a) **Summarised profit and loss accounts for the years ended 31 December**

	19X2		19X3		19X4	
	£'000	£'000	£'000	£'000	£'000	£'000
Turnover		3,120		2,700		3,000
Materials	630		480		600	
Labour	480		480		600	
Overhead	390		420		450	
		(1,500)		(1,380)		(1,650)
Gross profit		1,620		1,320		1,350
Administrative expenses	780		690		720	
Distribution costs	750		570		690	
		(1,530)		(1,260)		(1,410)
Profit on ordinary activities before taxation		90		60		(60)

(b) **Extracts from balance sheet at 31 December**

	19X2		19X3		19X4	
	£'000	£'000	£'000	£'000	£'000	£'000
Fixed assets at net book value		1,170		1,110		1,050
Raw materials	300		300		300	
Work in progress and finished goods	480		450		480	
Debtors	390		420		450	
		1,170		1,170		1,230
		2,340		2,280		2,280
Creditors: Amounts falling due within one year (including bank overdraft)		(810)		(810)		(870)
Capital employed		1,530		1,470		1,410

(c)   No fixed assets were purchased or sold by Franklin plc between 19X2 and 19X4.

Complete the table below:

	19X2	*19X3*	*19X4*
Percentage to turnover:			
Gross profit			
Net profit			
Materials			
Labour			
Overhead			
Administration			
Distribution			
Percentage change in sales over previous year			
ROCE $\dfrac{\text{Profit before tax}}{\text{Total assets less current liabilities at year end}} \times 100$			
$\dfrac{\text{Turnover}}{\text{Fixed assets}}$			
Current ratio			
Quick ratio			
Stock turnover $\dfrac{\text{Cost of sales}}{\text{Year-end stock}}$			
Raw materials			
Stock turnover $\dfrac{\text{Cost of materials}}{\text{Year-end materials stock}}$			
Debtor collection period			

Task 7

Prepare a report to the board of directors of Mills Carpets Ltd analysing the profitability and liquidity of Franklin plc. Also include a section on the limitations of the data upon which you have prepared your analysis.

UNIT 8

PRACTICE DEVOLVED ASSESSMENT 1

QUESTIONS

PREPARING VAT RETURNS

Time allowed 1 hour

You work part-time as the bookkeeper and accounts clerk for a firm that supplies and fits kitchens in the south west London area. The business is shown as Simons Kitchens. One of your duties is to complete the quarterly VAT return for the period to 31 October 19X7.

The system that the business adopts is that when an order is placed for a kitchen then a deposit of £80 plus VAT at 17.5% is payable immediately. The remaining amount due is usually invoiced on the date of completion of the kitchen unless agreed otherwise with the client.

Task 1

The sales invoices and purchase invoices for the period have been passed on to you together with a memorandum from the owner of the business, Jean Simons, regarding various other aspects that she thinks will be relevant. These invoices and memorandum are in the Appendixes 1, 2 and 3 of this assessment. You are required to fill in the figures that would appear in boxes 1 to 9 on the VAT return from the information provided and write up the VAT account.

VAT account

£		£

VAT RETURN

Value Added Tax Return

For the period

For Official Use

HM Customs and Excise

Registration number   Period

You should be liable to a financial penalty if your completed return and all the VAT payable are not received by the due date.

Due date:

For Official Use

Your VAT Office telehpone number is

REMEMBER

You must include VAT due on EC transactions in boxes 2 & 3 if they occur on or after 1.1.93.

Before you fill in this form please read the notes on the back and the VAT leaflet 'Filling in your VAT return'. Fill in all boxes clearly in ink, and write 'none' where necessary. Don't put a dash or leave any box blank. If there are no pence write "00" in the pence column. Do not enter more than one amount in any box.

For official use			
VAT due in this period on sales and other outputs	1		
VAT due in this period on acquisitions from other EC Member States	2		
Total VAT due (the sume of boxes 1 and 2)	3		
VAT reclaimed in this period on purchases and other inputs (including acquisitions from the EC)	4		
(Difference between boxes 3 and 4)	5		
Total value of sales and all other outputs excluding any VAT, include your box 8 figure	6		00
Total value of purchases and all other inputs excluding any VAT, include your box 9 figure	7		00
Total value of all supplies of goods and related services, exlcuding any VAT, to other EC Member States	8		00
Total value of all acquisitions of goods and related services, excluding any VAT, from other EC Member States	9		00

Retail schemes. If you have used any of the schemes in the period covered by this return, enter the relevant letter(s) in this box.

If you are enclosing a payment please tick this box.

DECLARATION: You, or someone on your behalf, must sign below.

I __ ___ ___ ___ ___ ___ ___ ___ ___ declare that the
(Full name of signatory in BLOCK LETTERS)
information given above is true and complete.

Signature __ ___ ___ ___ ___ ___ Date __ ____ __19 __ __

A false declaration can result in prosecution.

CD 2859/N3(04/92)   F3790 (January 1983)

VAT 100

Task 2

Next week the business is due a control visit by a Customs and Excise officer. Jean has asked you to put in writing for her the purpose of such visits and any action that the officer might take if he disagrees with any tax returns that have been made.

MEMORANDUM

TO:

FROM:

DATE:

SUBJECT:

Task 3

Jean also has some further queries about VAT and VAT documentation that she would like clarified before the control visit. Write a memorandum to her on each of the following items.

(1)   What are exempt and zero rated supplies and am I likely to make such supplies in my line of business?

(2)   If any of my supplies are exempt or zero rated then how will this affect the calculation of VAT payable?

(3)   I am considering using surplus kitchen units that we have in stock to furnish a kitchen in a flat that I own. Will this have any VAT consequences?

(4)   One of my regular suppliers of electrical fittings has offered me goods on a sale or return basis. How would the VAT on such goods be dealt with?

(5)   I sometimes receive credit notes from suppliers for goods that I have returned. If the credit note is to serve as valid documentation for a reduction of VAT on purchases what information must it contain?

(6)   I sometimes buy goods for the business from my local hardware shop and I have noticed that the invoice only includes the total value of the goods and does not show the VAT separately. Is this valid for VAT purposes and if not what should I do about it?

(7)   If at any time in the future I were to sell my business as a going concern would this have any VAT implications?

(Your memorandum should be in proper memorandum format and written in the space below.)

MEMORANDUM

APPENDIX 1 - SALES INVOICES

SALES INVOICE

SIMONS KITCHENS
199 Waterhill Road
London
SW6 8IC

Tel: 071 492 8833

VAT reg no: 832 2056 66

Invoice number: 5535

Date: 22 August 19X7

To: Mr G R Wilson
                  73A Baldwin Rise
                  London
                  SW4

Deposit of £94 including VAT at 17.5%

SALES INVOICE

SIMONS KITCHENS
199 Waterhill Road
London
SW6 8IC

Tel: 071 492 8833

VAT reg no: 832 2056 66

Date: 22 August 19X7

Invoice number: 5536

To: Mrs J Jepson
                  28 Margrave Hill
                  London
                  SW11

	VAT rate	£
Work performed:		
To supply and fit white lacquered kitchen code LDW 57	17.5%	6,660.00
Less: Deposit paid 1 July 19X7	17.5%	80.00
		———
Total excluding VAT		6,580.00
VAT at 17.5%		1,151.50
		———
Total including VAT		7,731.50
		———

Terms: Strictly payable within 30 days.

SALES INVOICE

SIMONS KITCHENS
199 Waterhill Road
London
SW6 8IC

Tel: 071 492 8833

VAT reg no: 832 2056 66

Date: 13 September 19X7

Invoice number: 5537

To: Mr G R Wilson
                   73A Baldwin Rise
                   London
                   SW4

	VAT rate	£
Work performed:		
Supply and fitting of dark oak kitchen units code DO 81	17.5%	2,900.00
Less: Deposit paid on 15 July	17.5%	80.00
		———
Total excluding VAT		2,820.00
VAT at 17.5%		493.50
		———
Total including VAT		3,313.50
		———

Terms: Strictly payable within 30 days.

SALES INVOICE

SIMONS KITCHENS
199 Waterhill Road
London
SW6 8IC

Tel: 071 492 8833

VAT reg no: 832 2056 66

Date: 30 September 19X7

Invoice number: 5538

To: Ms F Clancy
                      21 Edale Drive
                      London
                      SW18

	VAT rate	*£*
Work performed:		
Supply and fitting of limed oak kitchen units and AEG appliances	17.5%	9,375.62
Less: Deposit paid on 14 July 19X7	17.5%	80.00
Total excluding VAT		9,295.62
VAT at 17.5%		1,626.74
Total including VAT		10,922.36

Terms: Strictly payable within 30 days.

SALES INVOICE

SIMONS KITCHENS
199 Waterhill Road
London
SW6 8IC

Tel: 071 492 8833

VAT reg no: 832 2056 66

Date: 2 November 19X7

Invoice number: 5540

To: Mr S Singh
                  28 High Street
                  London
                  SW8

	VAT rate	£
Work performed:		
Supply and fitting of medium oak kitchen units (code MO 54) and		
Hotpoint appliances completed on 28 October 19X7	17.5%	7,254.50
Total excluding VAT		7,254.50
VAT at 17.5%		1,269.54
Total including VAT		8,524.04

Terms: Strictly payable within 30 days.

APPENDIX 2 - PURCHASE INVOICES

MAGNUM KITCHENS
Tower Estate
London
SW6

VAT reg no: 892 6845 60

Date/tax point: 8 August 19X7

Invoice number: SK 52

To: Simons Kitchens
                   199 Waterhill Road
                   London
                   SW6 8IC

	VAT rate	£
Supply of:		
13 kitchen units medium oak	17.5%	2,100.00
17 kitchen units dark oak	17.5%	2,800.00
Total excluding VAT		4,900.00
VAT @ 17.5%		857.50
Total including VAT		5,757.50

Terms: Payable within 60 days.

Expense claim form - Jean Simons

	Net	VAT	Gross
Client entertaining (bill attached)	117.00	20.48	137.48

BROKEN HEART RESTAURANT
Middle Court
London
EC4

Date: 4 October 19X7

	£
3 × standard set lunch	96.00
Wine	21.00
	117.00
VAT at 17.5%	20.48
	137.48

Service is included.

ELLSE ELECTRICALS
9, Summer Way
London
SW19

VAT reg no: 834 3745 77

Invoice number: 92785

Date: 24 August 19X7

To: Simons Kitchens
                 199 Waterhill Road
                 London
                 SW6 8IC

	VAT rate	£
Supply of:		
AEG fridge/freezer	17.5%	359.00
Hotpoint washing machine	17.5%	269.00
Hotpoint tumble dryer	17.5%	199.00
Total excluding VAT		827.00
VAT @ 17.5%		141.83
Total including VAT		968.83

Terms: 2%/30 days
       net 60 days

ELLSE ELECTRICALS
9, Summer Way
London
SW19

VAT reg no: 834 3745 77

Invoice number: 92941

Date: 19 September 19X7

To: Simons Kitchens
                 199 Waterhill Road
                 London
                 SW6 8IC

TAX CERTIFICATE

No payment is necessary for these goods. Output tax has been accounted for on the supply.

	VAT rate	£
Supply of:		
10 samples of halogen downlighter bulbs (cost price		
£7.48 each excluding VAT) (9 charged, one free)	17.5%	67.32
Total excluding VAT		67.32
VAT		11.78
Total including VAT		79.10

Terms: 2%/30 days
        net 60 days

NICHOLAS BAINS & CO
Fairacre Trading Estate
London
SW14

VAT reg no: 032 5485 68

Date: 1 October 19X7

To: Simons Kitchens
                   199 Waterhill Road
                   London
                   SW6 8IC

	VAT rate	£
Supply of 11 units hand made - oak	17.5	3,100.00
Supply of 1 oak kitchen table	17.5	800.00
Total excluding VAT		3,900.00
VAT at 17.5%		682.50
Total including VAT		4,582.50

Terms: payable within 30 days

APPENDIX 3 - Memorandum to bookkeeper from Jean Simons

MEMORANDUM

TO: Bookkeeper

FROM: Jean Simons

DATE: 4 November 19X7

SUBJECT: **VAT return**

Thank you for your note of 16 August 19X7 explaining the errors that you believed were made in the previous VAT return. Having checked the figures I can confirm that the tax payable was understated by £2,700 and the tax allowable was understated by £2,500. Please take whatever action is necessary to deal with this.

I am not sure whether or not the write off of bad debts is relevant to the VAT return but I know that you will need to know about them for writing up the accounts. In the last three months I have had to admit that there are two debts that I am sure will never be paid. One was an amount of £3,287.65 (including VAT) from Mr James Smith who was invoiced on 27 June 19X7 (invoice number 5503). The other was £1,957.55 (including VAT) from Mrs P Taylor-Young invoiced on 2 February 19X7 (invoice number 5479).

PRACTICE CENTRAL

ASSESSMENT ACTIVITIES

QUESTIONS

BTC (June 1994)

Data

Until three years ago BTC, an accountancy training organisation, ran its own fleet of vans and delivered manuals to retailers and colleges. The decision was taken to concentrate on core activities and so several organisations were carefully considered before RD plc was selected to take on the responsibility for storing and delivering the manuals. It was agreed that RD would purchase the manuals from BTC at the recommended selling price, less an agreed discount. This ensures that RD would automatically benefit from future increases in the selling price of the manuals. The arrangement has worked well for both organisations and a good relationship has been established.

The managing director of RD has been satisfied with the profits that have been earned, but he is concerned with the efficiency of the transport operation. You, as the assistant accountant, have been asked to provide regular information to the general manager, who is responsible for all aspects of transportation. The general manager has always controlled this area by observing what he calls 'key ratios' which he sees as delivery costs and drivers' wages as a percentage of sales, sales per van and the number of deliveries. He believes that if these ratios are improving then the transport operation is working well. He is also a great believer that graphs help to clarify the statistics in any report.

Assessment tasks

TASK 1

Using the figures from Appendix 1 below, draw a multiple bar chart (sometimes called a compound bar chart) showing for each year:

(a)   the sales value of the manuals sold;

(b)   the van expenses;

(c)   the drivers' wages.

APPENDIX 1			
Years	1	2	3
Sales £s	200,000	222,200	272,630
Van expenses £s	14,000	15,000	18,000
As % of sales	7	6.7	6.6
Drivers' wages £s	52,000	56,600	68,150
As % of sales	26	25.5	25
No. of vans	3	3	4
Sales per van £s	66,667	74,067	68,158
No. of deliveries	1,000	1,100	1,400

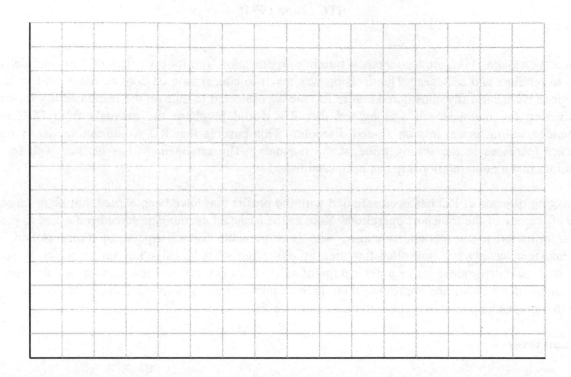

The accountant, although very interested in performance measures, is worried about the information in Appendix I. His main concern is that the selling prices of the manuals have increased dramatically over the last two years. This was due to BTC's policy of initially pricing below the normal market price and then, once the manuals had been accepted by the market, increasing prices quite sharply. The accountant wants to remove these specific price rises from the figures before calculating the 'key ratios' and has produced the following index numbers of price changes based on Year 1.

Years	*1*	*2*	*3*
Sales	100	110	137
Van expenses	100	104	106

Drivers' wages have shown very little change during these years and can remain as per Appendix 1.

TASK 2

Complete Appendix 2 below by:

(a)   Converting the actual figures for years 2 and 3 (from Appendix 1) to year 1 prices by using the price index given.

        (Calculations to the nearest £.)

(b)   Calculating the 'key ratios' including a new one of sales per delivery £s.

        (Calculations to 1 decimal place.)

APPENDIX 2			
Years	1	2	3
Sales £s	200,000		
Van expenses £s	14,000		
As % of sales	7		
Drivers' wages £s	52,000	56,600	68,150
As % of sales	26		
No. of vans	3	3	4
Sales per van £s	66,667		
No. of deliveries	1,000	1,100	1,400
Sales per delivery £s	200		

TASK 3

Write a report to the general manager commenting upon the performance of the transport operation. The report should be in three sections.

Section 1: should explain whether the 'key ratios' in Appendix 1 support the general manager's opinion;

Section 2: should explain whether the 'key ratios' in Appendix 2 indicate an efficient operation;

Section 3: (a) should state whether you consider that the transport operation is efficient and whether Appendix 1 or Appendix 2 should be the basis of future reports, giving reasons for your decisions;

         (b) should also suggest one other 'key ratio' that should be observed (no calculation is required) and say how often this type of information should be presented.

(AAT Jun 94)

WMSC (December 1994)

Data

The WMSC owns three ships which it offers for charter to three different markets. The first ship, the BB, is used for oil transportation; the second ship, the SS, is hired out to transport general cargo and the third ship, the TT, is used mainly for passenger transportation. The shipping industry has declined in recent years due to a surplus of ships and a fall in user demand. The world fleet has now fallen and there is evidence that the demand for charter ships is increasing.

ASSESSMENT TASKS

TASK 1

Complete the following Annual Operating Statement by calculating:

(a) the hire charges for TT as a percentage of the total hire charge;

(b) the four ratios for the total column.

Calculations should be to the nearest whole number.

Answer in the spaces provided.

ANNUAL OPERATING STATEMENT - WMSC - 1994								
		Total		*BB*		*SS*		*TT*
	%	£'000s	%	£'000s	%	£'000s	%	£'000s
Hire charges (Revenue)		8,263		4,512		2,429		1,322
As a % of total hire charge	-		55		29			
Voyage and operating costs		4,358		2,566		1,263		529
Gross profit		3,905		1,946		1,166		793
As a % of hire charges			43		48		60	
General expenses		2,720		1,378		903		439
Net profit		1,185		568		263		354
As a % of hire charges			13		11		27	
Capital employed		3,385		1,517		1,282		586
ROCE (Net profit to capital employed)			37		21		60	
Budgeted hire charges		10,200		5,000		4,000		1,200
Utilisation % $\left\{ \dfrac{\text{Hire charges}}{\text{Bud. hire charges}} \times 100 \right\}$			90		61		110	

TASK 2

Write a report to the General Manager of WMSC commenting on:

(a)   the overall performance of the company (using the figures and the ratios in the 'Total' column only). Shipping industry averages for last year were: ROCE 24%, gross profit to hire charges 40% and net profit to hire charges 15%;

(b)   the individual performance of each ship, stressing the good points revealed and those points that require investigation.

Funds are available for new investment and in the final section of the report you are asked to:

(c)   comment on a proposal to buy a second 'SS' to carry more general cargo;

(d)   suggest one non-financial factor that needs to be considered before another ship is purchased.

TASK 3

The administration manager of WMSC receives regular information on the analysis of the general expenses in the form of pie charts. He is having some difficulty in understanding the charts and, to make matters worse, when last month's charts were sent out the 'key' was not completed. You are asked to:

(a) use the figures provided to complete the key to the pie charts by identifying which segment (labelled A to E) represents which expense (eg, if you think A = depreciation, then write A opposite depreciation in the letter column.)

	November 1994 £'000	*November 1993* £'000
Wages and salaries	69	53
Building occupation costs	46	52
Agents' commission	58	42
General admin. expenses	23	31
Depreciation	34	32
	230	210

KEY

	Letter
Wages & salaries	------
Building occupation	------
Agents' commission	------
General admin. expenses	------
Depreciation	------

(b) write a short report to the administration manager:

  (i) explaining the main points that are revealed by a comparison of the pie charts;

  (ii) suggesting an explanation for the changes in the agents' commission and the general administration expenses.

ANSWERS

UNIT 7

PREPARING REPORTS AND RETURNS

CHAPTER 1

ANSWERS

BASIC MATHEMATICAL TECHNIQUES

Answer 1

(i) $\Sigma s = 4 + 3 + 6 + 5 + 4 = 22$
(ii) $\Sigma t = 5 + 4 + 1 + 2 + 6 = 18$
(iii) $\Sigma st = (4 \times 5) + (3 \times 4) + (6 \times 1) + (5 \times 2) + (4 \times 6) = 20 + 12 + 6 + 10 + 24 = 72$
(iv) $\Sigma s \Sigma t = 22 \times 18 = 396$

Answer 2

Price	*Quantity*	*Price × Quantity*
10	50	500
12	100	1,200
14	40	560
16	20	320
	210	2,580

Weighted average of prices $= \dfrac{2,580}{210}$ (£)

$= $ **£12.29**

Answer 3

	Product A Budget £	Actual £	% Change	Product B Budget £	Actual £	% Change
Sales	98,000	103,000	+ 5.1	14,000	20,000	+42.9
Material costs	(34,000)	(39,000)	+14.7	(4,600)	(7,200)	+56.5
Labour costs	(24,200)	(23,600)	− 2.5	(2,650)	(2,650)	0
Overheads	(24,200)	(20,000)	−17.4	(2,650)	(3,400)	+28.3
Contribution	15,600	20,400	+30.8	4,100	6,750	+64.6

CHAPTER 2

ANSWERS

TABULATION OF DATA

Answer 1

Alpha Products plc
Changes in labour force 19X7 to 19X8

	Department A			Department B			Total		
	19X7	*19X8*	*Change %*	*19X7*	*19X8*	*Change %*	*19X7*	*19X8*	*Change %*
Wage bill (£'000)	218	224	+2.8	295	313	+6.1	513	537	+4.7
Number employed	30	25	−16.7	42	43	+2.4	72	68	−5.6

(Source: Company records)

Answer 2

Waterson plc – Profit for the period 19X8 to 19X9

	Property division			Manufacturing division		
	19X8	*19X9*	*Increase %*	*19X8*	*19X9*	*Increase %*
Pre-tax profits (£'000)	12,141	15,426	27	8,343	9,271	11
Earnings per share (pence)	24.10	29.62	23	14.91	15.75	6
Dividend per share (pence)	11.52	13.50	17	8.86	9.63	9
Percentage total group profits	59	62		41	38	

(Source: Company records)

The table shows that the property division performed better than the manufacturing division in every respect.

The increase in earnings and dividends per share for the manufacturing division are probably not much above the general rate of inflation and therefore achieved practically no growth in real terms. The proportion of total contribution to profits by the property division is greater than that of the manufacturing division and is increasing.

Answer 3

Highest value is 77", lowest value is 61"; therefore, range of values = 16".

Taking class intervals as 60" and less than 63", 63" and less than 66", etc. the distribution becomes:

Class interval		Frequency
Height (inches)	*Tally*	*Number of students*
60" and less than 63"	l	1
63" and less than 66"	ll	2
66" and less than 69"	HHI HHI lll	13
69" and less than 72"	HHI HHI HHI HHI	20
72" and less than 75"	HHI HHI l	11
75" and less than 78"	lll	3
Total		50

Note: Take each item in the original table of raw data in the order in which it appears and place a tally mark in the appropriate class. That is, take 67 and put a tally mark against 66" and less than 69". Then take 71 and put a tally mark against 69" and less than 72". Do not go through the raw data picking out all the items in the first class, then go through it all again picking out all the items in the second class, etc. as this is much more time consuming and is more prone to mistakes.

Answer 4

The smallest value in the distribution is 105, the largest value in the distribution is 142. The range to be spanned is 142 − 105, ie. 37. The following grouping is a suggestion. The classes should be of equal width.

Group	Tally	Frequency
105 but less than 110	ll	2
110 but less than 115	HHl	5
115 but less than 120	llll	4
120 but less than 125	HHl lll	8
125 but less than 130	HHl HHl	10
130 but less than 135	HHl	5
135 but less than 140	llll	4
140 but less than 145	11	2
Total		40

Answer 5

UK Merchant Fleet 19X3 to 19X5

	Number of vessels				Gross tonnage ('000)			
			Change				Change	
Type of vessel	19X3	19X5	Actual	%	19X3	19X5	Actual	%
Passenger	86	85	−1	−1.2	573	626	+53	+9.2
Tanker	329	257	−72	−21.9	10,030	6,812	−3,218	−32.1
Cargo liner	134	97	−37	−27.6	1,194	876	−318	−26.6
Container	64	55	−9	−14.1	1,613	1,559	−54	−3.3
Tramp	190	167	−23	−12.1	406	352	−54	−13.3
Bulk carrier	128	80	−48	−37.5	4,709	3,109	−1,600	−34.0
Total	931	741	−190	−20.4	18,525	13,334	−5,191	−28.0

Note: All data is for the month of April in each year.

Tutorial note: Percentages are not additive. Thus the total percentage in column 5 cannot be obtained by adding the percentages above it. It must be calculated from the actual change (−190) expressed as a percentage of the first total (931).

Answer 6

Arrange in numerical order:

$$501, 502, 503, 504, 504, 504, 505, 505, 506, 506, 507, 508$$

(a)   (i)   The median weight is $\dfrac{504+505}{2} = 504.5$ kg.

(ii)   The modal weight is 504 kg (it occurs three times).

(iii)   To make calculating the arithmetic mean easier subtract 500.

$$\text{Mean} = 500 + \frac{1+2+3+4+4+4+5+5+6+6+7+8}{12}$$

$$= 500 + \frac{55}{12}$$

$$= 504.58 \text{ kg}$$

(b)   Geometric mean of 501 and 508 $= \sqrt{501 \times 508}$

$= 504.49$ kg

(c)   Median becomes 504 kg. (The additional item appears at the beginning of the sequence.)

Mode remains as 504 kg.

Arithmetic mean:

The mean becomes $500 + \dfrac{55-5}{13} = 503.85$ kg.

Answer 7

(a)   Highest value = 469, Lowest value = 347, Range = 122.

Hence for 5 groups ($122 \div 5 = 24.4$), a class interval of 25 will be satisfactory

Production (units)	Tally	Frequency	Cumulative frequency
345 and less than 370	꜒꜒꜒1 ꜒꜒꜒1 ꜒꜒꜒1 1	16	16
370 and less than 395	꜒꜒꜒1 111	8	24
395 and less than 420	1111	4	28
420 and less than 445	1	1	29
445 and less than 470	꜒꜒꜒1 ꜒꜒꜒1 1	11	40
	Total	40	

(b)   **'Less than' ogive of weekly production**

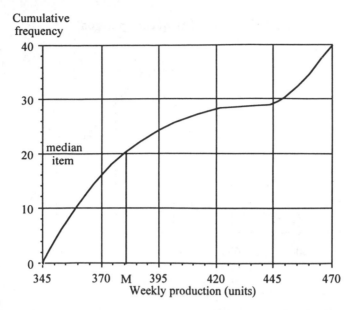

(c)   The median as read from the graph is 380 items.

(d)   The mean uses all the data and is therefore representative of all the data. It is easy to understand and calculate; it can be used in more advanced statistical theory.

It has the disadvantage that it can be unduly affected by a few extreme values, and it may not correspond to an actual value in the set if the set is discrete.

The median is also easy to understand. It is unaffected by extreme values, it can exist even if the items cannot be quantified, provided they can be ranked. It is a useful compromise between the mean and the mode.

As it does not use all the data, it may not be representative. Data has to be arranged in order of magnitude. It is not suitable for more advanced statistical theory.

Answer 8

(a)   14 cm
(b)   8 cm

Answer 9

(a) & (b)

Histogram and frequency polygon

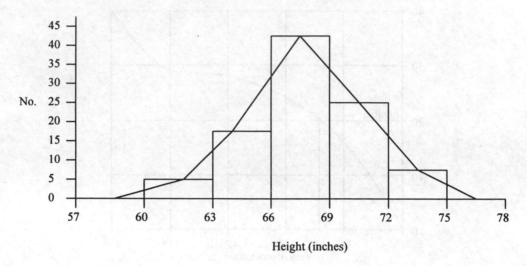

Note: the frequency polygon is achieved by joining up the mid-points of the histogram. Note the correct treatment of the two ends of the polygon.

(c)   **Ogive**

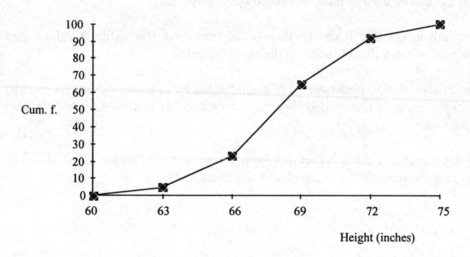

Note: the cumulative frequency is plotted against the upper class limit.

Answer 10

Find the mid point of each class interval, x, and produce a table showing x, f and fx.

Multiply (x) by (f) and calculate $\sum fx$.

Mid-value	Frequency	
x	f	fx
155	1	155
165	9	1,485
175	12	2,100
185	16	2,960
195	26	5,070
205	19	3,895
215	8	1,720
225	6	1,350
235	2	470
245	1	245
Totals	$\sum f = 100$	$\sum fx = 19,450$

Calculate the arithmetic mean.

$$\text{The arithmetic mean} = \frac{\sum fx}{\sum f} = \frac{19,450}{100} = 194.5 \text{ cms}$$

Notice that, if the original data had units so the mean should have units.

It might be worth practising calculating means on your scientific calculator.

Answer 11

Calculate the cumulative frequency = 1, 10, 22, 38, 64, 83, 91, 97, 99, 100.

$$\text{Median} = \frac{100}{2} = 50\text{th item}$$

The median class is 190 to 200 ie, where the cumulative frequency will equal 50.

$L_m = 190$ cm, $C_m = 10$ cm, n = 100, $F_{m-1} = 1 + 9 + 12 + 16 = 38$, $f_m = 26$

$$\text{Median} = L_m + \frac{C_m(\frac{1}{2}n - F_{m-1})}{f_m}$$

$$= 190 + \frac{10 \times (50 - 38)}{26}$$

$$= 194.62 \text{ cm}$$

Answer 12

The mode can be calculated by drawing a histogram; however, if solved using the formula, the result would be more accurate.

The formula to calculate the mode   = $L_m + \dfrac{C_m(f_m - f_{m-1})}{2f_m - (f_{m-1} + f_{m+1})}$

where L_m =   190 cm
         C_m =   10 cm
         f_m =   26
         f_{m-1} =   16
         f_{m+1} =   19

The mode will be nearer 200 cm than 190 cm.

The mode   = $190 + \dfrac{10 \times (26 - 16)}{(2 \times 26) - (16 + 19)}$

$$190 + \dfrac{100}{52 - 35}$$

195.88 cm

CHAPTER 3

ANSWERS

DIAGRAMMATIC PRESENTATION

Answer 1

Component bar charts

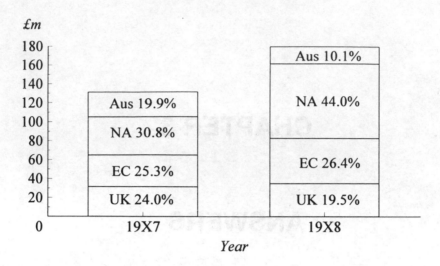

Annual sales 19X7 to 19X8

Tutorial notes

(1)   Once the chart has been completed the lefthand scale can be erased.
(2)   If there is no room to write the details in each section, use shading and a key.

Answer 2

Multiple bar chart

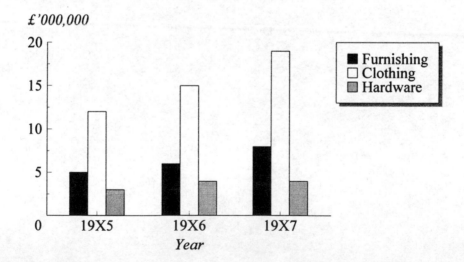

Departmental sales 19X5 to 19X7

Answer 3

Pie charts

Workings

Angles required to represent the given data for the two years are as follows:

	19X6	Degrees	19X7	Degrees
United Kingdom	1,760	209	1,800	171
EC countries (other than UK)	576	68	612	58
Other European countries	214	25	374	35
North and South America	306	36	354	34
CIS	54	7	72	7
Other overseas countries	127	15	584	55
	3,037	360	3,796	360

The total area of the pies will be proportionate to the 19X6 total sales figure of 3,037 and the 19X7 total sales figure of 3,796, ie:

3,037 : 3,796 or 1 : 1.25

Thus the radii of the pies will be proportionate to the square root of these numbers, ie:

$$\sqrt{1} = 1$$

$$\sqrt{1.25} = 1.12$$

If a radius of 2 cm is assumed for 19X6, then the radius of the 19X7 pie will be:

2 cm × 1.12 = 2.24 cm

19X6

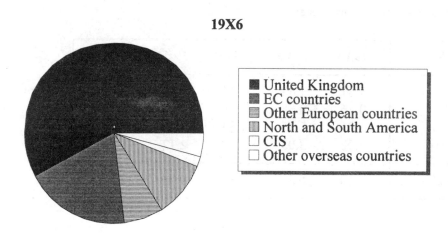

19X7

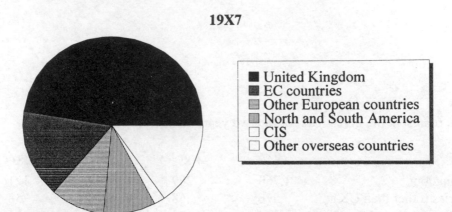

United Kingdom
EC countries
Other European countries
North and South America
CIS
Other overseas countries

Answer 4

(a)   Before drawing any diagram it is necessary to calculate the actual sales by product groups, as only the percentage sales are given in the question.

For 19X5		£m
Product A	24% of 6.3 = $\dfrac{24}{100} \times 6.3 =$	1.51
Product B	12% of 6.3 = $\dfrac{12}{100} \times 6.3 =$	0.76
Product C	16% of 6.3 = $\dfrac{16}{100} \times 6.3 =$	1.01
Others	48% of 6.3 = $\dfrac{48}{100} \times 6.3 =$	3.02
Total		6.30

Similar calculations are necessary for the years 19X4 to 19X1 inclusive.

Showing this in a tabular form gives:

Product	19X5	19X4	19X3	19X2	19X1
A	1.51	1.43	1.16	0.94	0.58
B	0.76	0.65	0.64	0.42	0.47
C	1.01	1.37	1.33	1.22	1.17
Others	3.02	3.05	2.67	2.12	1.68
Total	6.30	6.50	5.80	4.70	3.90

This information can now be displayed in a bar chart.

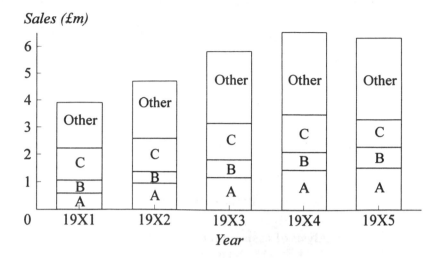

Sales by product groups, 19X1 to 19X5

(b)   In order to analyse the total sales for each of the two years 19X4 and 19X5, it is necessary to consider the relative proportions of cost, taxation and profit.

	19X4			*19X5*	
Direct materials	$\frac{3.2}{6.5} \times 100 =$	49.2%		$\frac{3.1}{6.3} \times 100 =$	49.2%
Direct wages	$\frac{1.2}{6.5} \times 100 =$	18.5%		$\frac{1.4}{6.3} \times 100 =$	22.2%
Production overhead	$\frac{1.0}{6.5} \times 100 =$	15.4%		$\frac{1.0}{6.3} \times 100 =$	15.9%
Other overhead	$\frac{0.4}{6.5} \times 100 =$	6.2%		$\frac{0.4}{6.3} \times 100 =$	6.3%
Taxation	$\frac{0.3}{6.5} \times 100 =$	4.6%		$\frac{0.3}{6.3} \times 100 =$	4.8%
Profit	$\frac{0.4}{6.5} \times 100 =$	6.2%		$\frac{0.1}{6.3} \times 100 =$	1.6%
Totals		100.1%			100.0%

(due to rounding)

This information can now be best expressed in two pie charts.

In order to calculate the angles of the sectors, remember 100% is represented by 360°, therefore, every 1% is represented by 3.6°.

Analysis of costs, taxation and profit 19X4

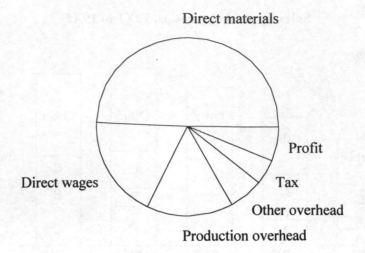

Analysis of costs, taxation and profit 19X5

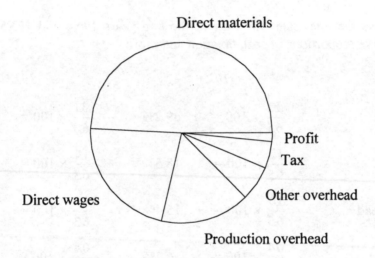

To emphasise direct wages, this sector could be 'exploded', ie. shown as if partially separated from the rest of the pie, or shaded more heavily than the other sectors.

Comments

The most noticeable differences between the two years are:

(i)   *Direct wages* – these have risen from 18.5% of sales in 19X4 to 22.2% of sales in 19X5. An increase of 3.7%.

(ii)   *Profit* – this has fallen from 6.2% of sales in 19X4 to 1.6% of sales in 19X5. A decrease of 4.6%.

All other percentages compare very favourably – 0.5% being the largest difference apart from those noted above.

The increase in direct wages, etc. in 19X5 has resulted in a fall in profits. (This is true in absolute and relative terms.)

CHAPTER 4

ANSWERS

GRAPHICAL PRESENTATION

Answer 1

Month 19X5	Monthly sales £'000	Cumulative monthly sales £'000		Moving annual total* £'000
January	18		= 18	239
February	21	21 + 18	= 39	240
March	26	39 + 26	= 65	241
April	16	65 + 16	= 81	239
May	20	81 + 20	= 101	243
June	26	101 + 26	= 127	244
July	24	127 + 24	= 151	250
August	28	151 + 28	= 179	261
September	28	179 + 28	= 207	270
October	32	207 + 32	= 239	284
November	33	239 + 33	= 272	298
December	41	272 + 41	= 313	313

* Moving annual totals are easy to calculate, being simply the total of 12 months' figures.

239 is the total of the 12 months from February 19X4 to January 19X5 inclusive.
240 is the total of the 12 months from March 19X4 to February 19X5 inclusive.

The 240 is found by omitting the February 19X4 value (20) and including the February 19X5 value (21) instead, giving an increase of 1 to 240.

241 is the total of the 12 months from April 19X4 to March 19X5 inclusive.

Omit 25 and include 26 instead, an increase of 1, giving 241, etc.

They are called moving annual totals because the initial month moves on one each time.

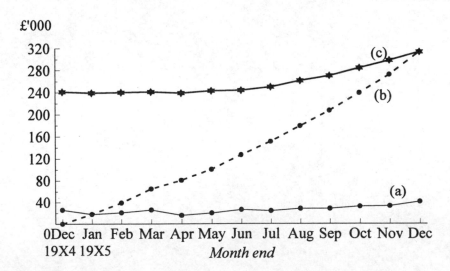

All points are plotted at the end of their time intervals since they are totals rather than averages.

Line (a) starts at the December 19X4 figure of 26.

Line (b) starts at zero.

Line (c) starts at 241 which is the total of sales up to the end of December 19X4.

Since the moving annual total is the total of the preceding 12 months' sales, the moving annual total for December 19X5 must be the same as the cumulative monthly total up to December 19X5 and the two lines will meet at this point.

The graph (a) shows that sales tended to be higher in autumn and early winter than for the rest of the year.

Graph (c) shows that sales were approximately the same as in the previous year for the first half of the year because it is horizontal, but steadily improved on the previous year's performance over the second half of the year because this part of the graph is rising.

Answer 2

Month	19X8/19X9	19X9/19Y0	Cumulative total 19X9/19Y0	Moving annual total 19X9/19Y0
June	600	700	700	7,800
July	500	600	1,300	7,900
August	600	600	1,900	7,900
September	600	700	2,600	8,000
October	700	900	3,500	8,200
November	800	1,000	4,500	8,400
December	900	1,000	5,500	8,500
January	600	700	6,200	8,600
February	400	500	6,700	8,700
March	600	700	7,400	8,800
April	600	700	8,100	8,900
May	800	900	9,000	9,000

Tutorial note: The moving annual total is the total for 12 months up to and including the current month, hence:

Moving annual total for June 19X9 = Total from July 19X8 to June 19X9 inclusive
Moving annual total for July 19X9 = Moving annual total for previous month − 500 + 600, etc.

Note that the final moving annual total value must equal the final cumulative total value.

Z chart of sales, AT Photographic Company June 19X9 to May 19Y0

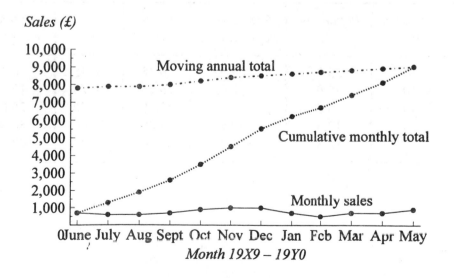

Answer 3

Range £	Number of orders	% of total	Cumulative %	Sales value £	% of total	Cumulative %
< 50	322	46	46	10,800	9	9
50 & < 100	245	35	81	18,000	15	24
100 & < 500	77	11	92	18,000	15	39
500 & <1,000	35	5	97	30,000	25	64
1,000 & <2,500	21	3	100	43,200	36	100
Total	700	100		120,000	100	

Distribution of sales among orders

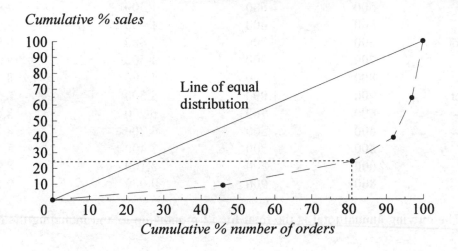

Answer 4

(a)   It is first necessary to calculate the percentages and hence the cumulative percentages for each of the variables under consideration.

(i)   Before tax and benefits

Population m	Population %	Cumulative population %	Income £m	Income %	Cumulative income %
10	25.0	25.0	6.25	6.25	6.25
10	25.0	50.0	6.25	6.25	12.50
10	25.0	75.0	12.50	12.50	25.00
5	12.5	87.5	25.00	25.00	50.00
5	12.5	100.0	50.00	50.00	100.00

(ii)   After tax and benefits   CITY OF LIVERPOOL COMMUNITY COLLEGE

Population cumulative %	Income £m	Income %	Cumulative income %
25.0	9.375	12.5	12.5
50.0	9.375	12.5	25.0
75.0	18.750	25.0	50.0
87.5	18.750	25.0	75.0
100.0	18.750	25.0	100.0

Both these sets of figures are now plotted on the same graph along with the line of equal distribution.

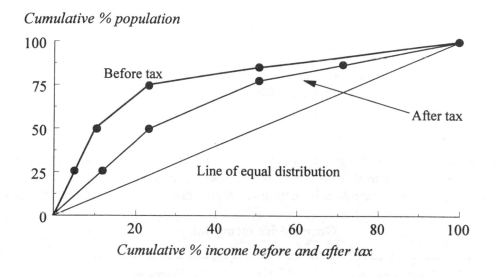

(b)   The purpose of a Lorenz curve is to show graphically the extent to which a variable is distributed throughout the population. It gives a picture of the divergence from average – ie. from the line of equal distribution which shows what the variable would look like if it were equally distributed throughout the population.

The 'before tax' curve is further away from the line of equal distribution than the 'after tax' curve. This indicates that when tax and benefits are taken into account a more equal distribution of income exists amongst the population than before.

The inequality can be measured by the area enclosed by the curve and the line of equal distribution. This is called the 'area of inequality. and the greater this area, the greater the inequality of distribution.

Alternatively, the point on each curve that is furthest from the line of equal distribution can be quoted. In the above example, before tax, the lower 75% of the population had 25% of the total income, while after tax, the lower 66% had 39%.

Tutorial note: Lorenz curves always require the numerical data to be in percentage terms.

Answer 5

(a) & (b)   **Scattergraph of advertising expenditure and newspaper circulation**

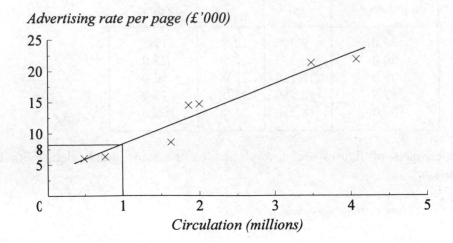

Advertising rate per page (£'000)

Circulation (millions)

(c)   Using the graph above, the approximate advertising expenditure per page for an expected circulation of 1 million would be £8,000.

Answer 6

(a)   **Tutorial note:** The range of values is from 1.7 to 9.0. A convenient number of groups will therefore be 10, from 0–1, 1–2, etc. but choose the intervals so that there is no ambiguity about boundary values. As the data is continuous, there must be no gaps between the group boundaries.

Grouped frequency table

Time (minutes)	Tally	Frequency
0 and less than 1		0
1 and less than 2	l	1
2 and less than 3	ll	2
3 and less than 4	lll	3
4 and less than 5	llll	5
5 and less than 6	llll llll	10
6 and less than 7	llll l	6
7 and less than 8	llll	4
8 and less than 9	lll	3
9 and less than 10	l	1
Total		35

(b)   **Histogram of times to complete operation**

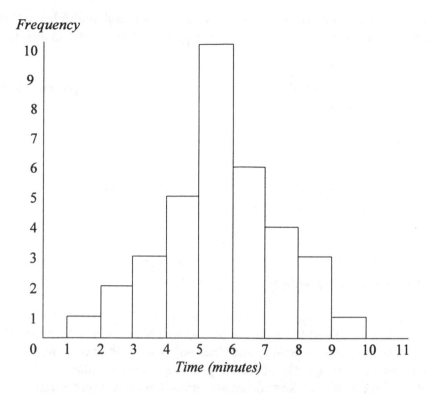

(c)

Time	Frequency	Cumulative frequency
0 & < 1	0	0
1 & < 2	1	1
2 & < 3	2	3
3 & < 4	3	6
4 & < 5	5	11
5 & < 6	10	21
6 & < 7	6	27
7 & < 8	4	31
8 & < 9	3	34
9 & < 10	1	35

Ogive of operation times

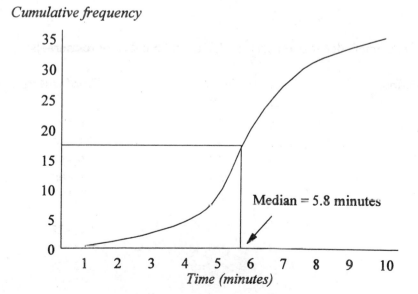

Answer 7

(a)   Bar charts (simple, component, percentage component and multiple) are statistical diagrams of general use for displaying data in absolute or relative forms. Bar charts are widely used in most media.

A histogram is a statistical diagram specifically used to represent grouped (or ungrouped) frequency distributions.

These uses are not interchangeable.

Both diagrams involve rectangles being used to represent a quantity, and in both it is enclosed area that is the basis of representation. Except in multiple bar charts, in bar charts there ought always to be spaces between bars; there should never be spaces left between the bars in a histogram.

(b)   The mean value of a quantity that varies is the arithmetical average; the mode is the most popular or frequent value and the median is the middle value when all values are ranked. Each is referred to as an average, with possibly misleading consequences.

The mean is the only measure to take account of all values of the quantity and to be simply represented mathematically. As such it has great application in the subject of statistics. The mode may not exist, may not be unique and does not find much favour with statisticians. Neither the mode nor median are greatly affected by a few extreme values, unlike the mean. When the distribution of a quantity is skewed, the median is thus more appropriate.

(c)   Whether the index is to be used to indicate change in average price, average volume or average value, the following considerations must be made when devising a new index:

(i)   What is the purpose of the index?

(ii)   What items should be covered by the index?

(iii)   How frequently should the index be calculated?

(iv)   When/where should the index be based?

(v)   Should the index be weighted and, if so, should the weights be those of the base period, of the current period, or not particularly related to time at all?

Answer 8

(a)   Total number of customers depends on class midpoint and number of restaurants:

Class midpoint	No. of restaurants		Total visiting customers	
	A	B	A	B
175	7	3	1,225	525
225	62	11	13,950	2,475
275	34	58	9,350	15,950
400	19	84	7,600	33,600
750	3	24	2,250	18,000
			34,375	70,550

(b)   A Lorenz curve consists of a plot of one cumulative percentage against another cumulative percentage.   In this case two curves, A and B, should be calculated and plotted of percentage cumulative customers against percentage cumulative turnover:

Total customers		% Customers		Cumulative % customers		Turnover £		% Turnover		Cumulative % turnover	
A	B	A	B	A	B	A	B	A	B	A	B
1,225	525	3.6	0.7	3.6	0.7	1,620	6,800	1.0	2.0	1.0	2.0
13,950	2,475	40.6	3.5	44.2	4.2	21,640	19,380	13.4	5.7	14.4	7.7
9,350	15,950	27.2	22.6	71.4	26.8	35,690	109,140	22.1	32.1	36.5	39.8
7,600	33,600	22.1	47.6	93.5	74.4	58,950	147,560	36.5	43.4	73.0	83.2
2,250	18,000	6.5	25.5	100.0	99.9	43,600	57,120	27.0	16.8	100.0	100.0
34,375	70,550	100.0	99.9			161,500	340,000	100.0	100.0		

Lorenz curves: Companies A and B

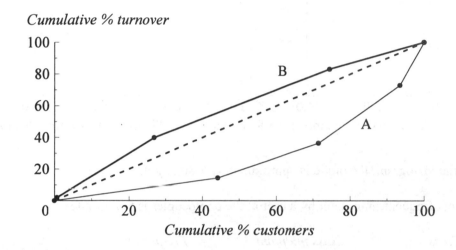

(c)   Curve A has greater curvature than curve B; curve A is below the line of equality of distribution, curve B is above. Thus, a greater percentage of A's customers than of B's customers is required to contribute a given percentage of total turnover for the two companies. Total weekly turnover for B is slightly over twice that for A; B's customers spend more than A's customers generally, per visit.

Answer 9

(a)   A frequency distribution of photocopying times with six classes:

Class	Tally	Frequency (No. of uses)
0.0 to under 2.0	HHH ll	7
2.0 to under 4.0	HHH llll	9
4.0 to under 6.0	HHH HHH HHH l	16
6.0 to under 8.0	HHH HHH HHH	15
8.0 to under 10.0	HHH lll	8
10.0 to under 12.0	HHH	5
Total		60

The frequency distribution is almost bell-shaped, symmetrical, having a slight positive skewness.

(b)

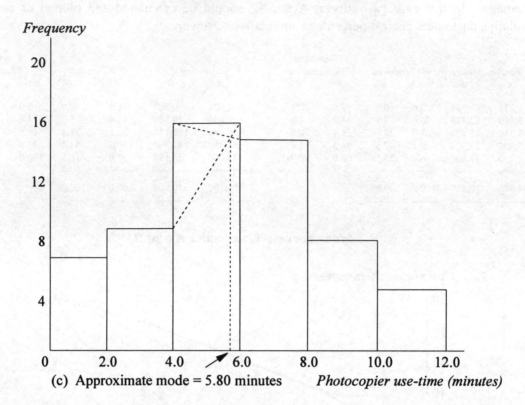

Histogram: No. of uses v Use-time

(c) Approximate mode = 5.80 minutes

(c)   From the histogram, the mode is approximately 5.80 minutes.

The most frequent time spent by a user at the photocopier is 5.8 minutes.

(d)

Class	Class midpoint x	Frequency f	fx
0 – < 2	1.0	7	7
2 – < 4	3.0	9	27
4 – < 6	5.0	16	80
6 – < 8	7.0	15	105
8 – < 10	9.0	8	72
10 – < 12	11.0	5	55
		60	346

$$\text{Mean use-time} = \frac{346}{60} = 5.77 \text{ minutes}$$

CHAPTER 5

ANSWERS

TIME SERIES ANALYSIS

Activity 1

(a)   **Appliance sales 19X1 to 19Y0**

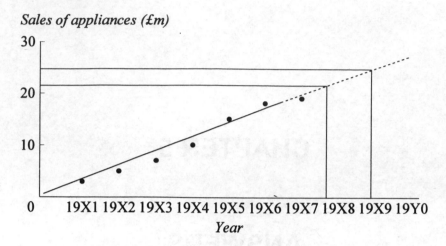

(b)   Reading from the extrapolated appliance sales line, forecast of sales for 19X8 is £23m and for 19X9 is £26m.

(c)   **Policy sales and appliance sales**

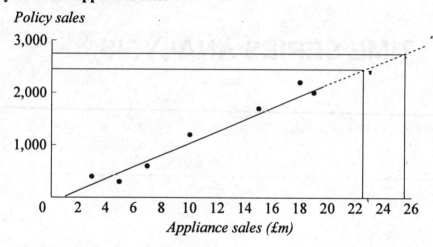

(d)   From the graph the predictions are:

      19X8   Sales £23m   Policies 2,500
      19X9   Sales £26m   Policies 2,800

Both graphs are subject to error due to the scatter in the points, but the scatter is sufficiently contained to suggest that a linear relationship is justified in both cases. However, both predictions are based on extrapolations which assume the linear relationship is going to continue in the future. There is no guarantee that this will be the case. Bearing this in mind, the forecasts would be sufficiently accurate to be useful for planning purposes, but the forecasts for 19X9 will be less reliable than those for 19X8, as the extrapolation was made over a longer time period.

Activity 2

(a)   Seasonal variation – high in summer, low in winter
(b)   Rising trend
(c)   Seasonal variation – high in autumn/winter, low in summer
(d)   Cyclical variation (affected by booms and depressions)
(e)   Decreasing trend
(f)   Residual (random) variation

Activity 3

First, it is advisable to draw a graph of the time series so that an overall picture can be gained and the cyclical movements seen.

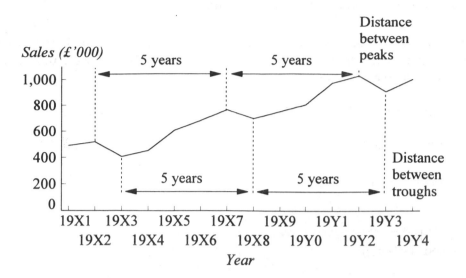

In order to calculate the trend figures it is necessary to establish the span of the cycle. From the graph it can easily be seen that the distance in time between successive peaks (and successive troughs) is five years; therefore a five-point moving average must be calculated. No other type of average will smooth out the five yearly cycle of fluctuations.

A table of the following form is now drawn up:

Year	Sales £'000	Five yearly moving total	Five yearly moving average
19X1	491	–	–
19X2	519	–	–
19X3	407	2,476	495
19X4	452	2,666	533
19X5	607	2,911	582
19X6	681	3,200	640
19X7	764	3,499	700
19X8	696	3,694	739
19X9	751	3,983	797
19Y0	802	4,245	849
19Y1	970	4,452	890
19Y2	1,026	4,699	940
19Y3	903	–	–
19Y4	998	–	–

(Tutorial notes on the calculation

(a)   As the name implies, the five yearly moving total is the sum of successive groups of five years' sales, ie:

$$491 + 519 + 407 + 452 + 607 \quad = \quad 2,476$$

Then advancing by one year:

$$519 + 407 + 452 + 607 + 681 \quad = \quad 2,666, \text{ etc. until, for the last five years}$$

$$802 + 970 + 1,026 + 903 + 998 = \quad 4,699$$

It is not necessary to add five values each time. For the second total, 491 is omitted and 681 included instead, hence the total will increase by 190. Similarly, for the third total omit 519 and include 764, an increase of 245 and so on.

(b)   These moving totals are simply divided by five to give the moving averages, ie:

$$2,476 \div 5 = 495$$

$$2,666 \div 5 = 533$$

$$|$$

$$|$$

$$|$$

$$4,699 \div 5 = 940$$

(c)   Averages are always plotted in the middle of the time period, ie. 495 is the average of the figures for 19X1, 19X2, 19X3, 19X4 and 19X5 and so it is plotted at the end of 19X3, this being the mid-point of the time interval from the end of 19X1 to the end of 19X5. Similarly, 533 is plotted at the end of 19X4 and 940 is plotted at the end of 19Y2.)

A second graph is now drawn showing the original figures again and the trend figures, ie. the five yearly moving averages.

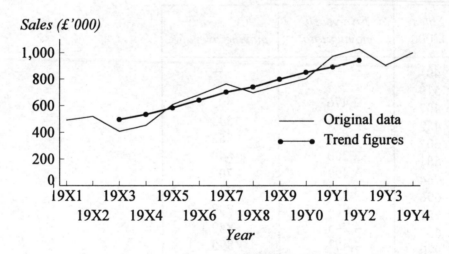

Note how the fluctuations have been smoothed out. This is only achieved if each average is calculated over a complete cycle, in this example a five yearly one.

Activity 4

Malcan plc

Day	Output A	Five day total (centred on the middle day)	Trend T
Monday	187		
Tuesday	203		
Wednesday	208	1,022	204
Thursday	207	1,042	208
Friday	217	1,047	209
Monday	207	1,049	210
Tuesday	208	1,048	210
Wednesday	210	1,043	209
Thursday	206	1,038	208
Friday	212	1,040	208
Monday	202	1,042	208
Tuesday	210	1,041	208
Wednesday	212	1,043	209
Thursday	205	1,049	210
Friday	214	1,054	211
Monday	208	1,059	212
Tuesday	215	1,071	214
Wednesday	217	1,070	214
Thursday	217		
Friday	213		

(a)   Note that in calculating the trend, which is the average of the five day total, it is centred on the third day in every group of five because the cycle consists of an odd number of periods.

(b)

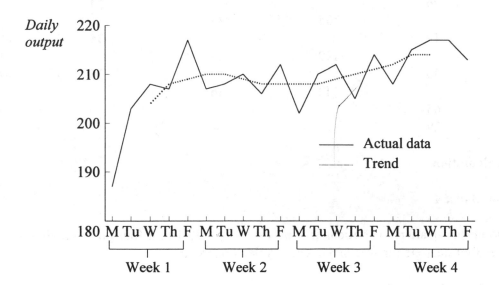

Activity 5

It is necessary to draw up a table as follows:

1 Year and quarter	2 Takings (£'000) A	3 Moving annual total	4 Four quarterly moving average	5 Centred value T	6 A − T
1	13		–	–	–
2	22			–	–
		116	29		
19X1 3	58			30	28
		119	30		
4	23			31	−8
		125	31		
1	16			32	−16
		128	32		
2	28			33	−5
		130	33		
19X2 3	61			33	28
		131	33		
4	25			33	−8
		132	33		
1	17			33	−16
		132	33		
2	29			33	−4
		133	33		
19X3 3	61			34	27
		134	34		
4	26			34	−8
		135	34		
1	18			35	−17
		139	35		
2	30			36	−6
19X4		142	36		
3	65			–	–
4	29		–	–	–

Notes on the calculation

(a)   *Columns 3 and 4*

To smooth out quarterly variations it is necessary to calculate a four-point moving average, since there are four quarters (or seasons) in each cycle of one year.

ie. $\dfrac{13 + 22 + 58 + 23}{4} = \dfrac{116}{4} = 29$

then, advancing by one quarter:

$$\frac{22 + 58 + 23 + 16}{4} \quad = \quad \frac{119}{4} \quad = \quad 30 \text{ (rounding up to nearest whole number)}$$

$$\frac{18 + 30 + 65 + 29}{4} \quad = \quad \frac{142}{4} \quad = \quad 36 \text{ (rounding up to nearest whole number)}$$

In the table this is done in two stages. The total of the four quarterly values is obtained in column 3, headed *Moving annual total* and these values are then divided by four to find the moving average.

(b)   29 is the average of the figures for the four quarters of 19X1 and so if plotted, would be at the mid-point of the interval from the end of the first quarter to the end of the fourth quarter, ie. half-way through the third quarter of 19X1. These averages do not therefore correspond with the times at which the original figures occur. This will always be the case when the cycle has an even number of periods.

(c)   *Column 5*

So that the original figures and the trend figures coincide chronologically, the moving averages are centred:

ie. $$\frac{29 + 30}{2} \quad = \quad 30 \text{ (rounding up)}$$

$$\frac{30 + 31}{2} \quad = \quad 31 \text{ (rounding up)}$$

$$\frac{35 + 36}{2} \quad = \quad 36 \text{ (rounding up)}$$

The first average now corresponds in time with the original value for the third quarter and so on.

These are the trend values.

(d)   *Column 6*

The figures for column 6 are the differences between the actual figures and the centred values, ie. A   T, which equals S+R.

ie. $58 - 30 = 28$
        $23 - 31 = -8$

        $30 - 36 = -6$

(e)   In order to remove the residual variation (R) and establish the quarterly variation (S), another table must be drawn up:

	Quarter 1	Quarter 2	Quarter 3	Quarter 4
	–	–	28	–8
	–16	–5	28	–8
	–16	–4	27	–8
	–17	–6	–	–
Totals	–49	–15	83	–24
Seasonal variation	–16	–5	28	–8

The individual variations have been averaged out for each quarter of the cycle:

ie.   Quarter 1 $\dfrac{-16+(-16)+(-17)}{3}$ $=$ $\dfrac{-49}{3}$ $=$ -16

       Quarter 2 $\dfrac{-5+(-4)+(-6)}{3}$ $=$ $\dfrac{-15}{3}$ $=$ -5

and so on

(f)   The quarterly variations should total to zero again but $-16 + (-5) + 28 + (-8) = -1$. However, the adjustment would only be $-1 \div 4$, ie. -0.25 and since the figures are whole numbers this would make no appreciable difference to the result. To avoid fractions, the largest value (28) is increased by 1 to 29.

∴ Quarterly variation (S):

1st   quarter $= -16$
2nd   quarter $= -5$
3rd   quarter $= 29$
4th   quarter $= -8$

These values will be the same each year.

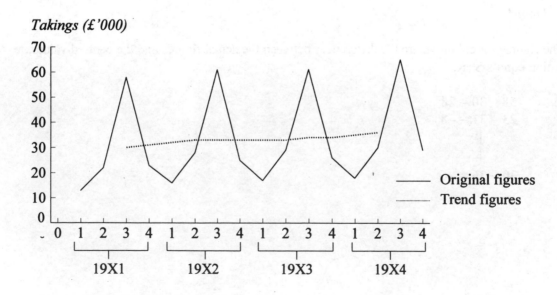

Comment

As can be seen from the calculations and the graph, the takings show a slight upward trend and the seasonal (quarterly) variations are considerable.

Activity 6

Forecasting of births

Calculation of trend

Year	Quarter	Births	Moving annual total	Four-quarterly moving average	Centred values = trend	Actual – Trend
1	1	162				
	2	163				
			639	159.75		
	3	164			158.9	+5.1
			632	158.00		
	4	150			157.1	−7.1
			625	156.25		
2	1	155			154.9	+0.1
			614	153.50		
	2	156			152.2	+3.8
			604	151.00		
	3	153			150.5	+2.5
			600	150.00		
	4	140			149.2	−9.2
			594	148.50		
3	1	151			147.8	+3.2
			588	147.00		
	2	150			146.6	+3.4
			585	146.25		
	3	147			–	–
				–		
	4	137			–	–

easonal adjustments

	Quarter 1	Quarter 2	Quarter 3	Quarter 4
1	–	–	+5.1	–7.1
2	+0.1	+3.8	+2.5	–9.2
3	+3.2	+3.4	–	–
Total	+3.3	+7.2	+7.6	–16.3
Average	+1.65	+3.6	+3.8	–8.15
Adjustment	–0.225	–0.225	–0.225	–0.225
Seasonal movement	+1.425	+3.375	+3.575	–8.375
Rounded	+1	+3	+4	–8

Tutorial notes

(1)   The four-quarterly moving average is the average of the four quarterly values moving down one quarter at a time.

(2)   The adjustment to the average in the second table is to make the total of the four averages equal to zero.

CHAPTER 6

ANSWERS

INDEX NUMBERS

Answer 1

Year	Price relative	Quantity relative
19X1	100	100
19X2	$\frac{125}{120} \times 100 = 104.2$	$\frac{5.2}{5.3} \times 100 = 98.1$
19X3	$\frac{131}{120} \times 100 = 109.2$	$\frac{5.0}{5.3} \times 100 = 94.3$

Comments

The price increased by 4.2% from 19X1 to 19X2 and by 9.2% in the two year period from 19X1 to 19X3. Sales quantities decreased by 1.9% from 19X1 to 19X2 and by 5.7% in the two year period from 19X1 to 19X3. Thus as price increased, quantity sold decreased. This does not necessarily mean that increase in price was the direct cause of the decrease in sales. It may be that both were caused by other factors such as inflation combined with economic depression.

Answer 2

(a)   **Laspeyre index**

Item	Weight (q_0)	19X4 Price (p_0)	£ $p_0 \times q_0$	19X5 Price (p_1)	£ $p_1 \times q_0$
Milk	50,000	19p	9,500	26p	13,000
Bread	30,000	39p	11,700	40p	12,000
Soap	20,000	42p	8,400	64p	12,800
Sugar	10,000	60p	6,000	68p	6,800
Eggs	3,000	84p	2,520	72p	2,160
			38,120		46,760

$\Sigma p_1 q_0$ = 46,760 = buying pattern in 19X4 at 19X5 prices

$\Sigma p_0 q_0$ = 38,120 = buying pattern in 19X4 at 19X4 prices

$\therefore$ Index = $\dfrac{\Sigma p_1 q_0}{\Sigma p_0 q_0} \times 100$

  = $\dfrac{46,760}{38,120} \times 100$

  = 122.7

The cost of buying 19X4 quantities at 19X5 prices shows an increase of 22.7% over the cost of buying those quantities at 19X4 prices.

(b)   **Paasche index**

Item	Weight (q_1)	Price (p_0)	£ $p_0 \times q_1$	Price (p_1)	£ $p_1 \times q_1$
Milk	70,000	19p	13,300	26p	18,200
Bread	40,000	39p	15,600	40p	16,000
Soap	25,000	42p	10,500	64p	16,000
Sugar	8,000	60p	4,800	68p	5,440
Eggs	2,500	84p	2,100	72p	1,800
			46,300		57,440

$\sum p_0 q_1$ =   46,300 =   buying pattern in 19X5 at 19X4 prices

$\sum p_1 q_1$ =   57,440 =   buying pattern in 19X5 at 19X5 prices

$\therefore$ Index   = $\dfrac{57,440}{46,300} \times 100$

   =   124.1

The 19X5 index shows an increase of 24.1% over buying 19X5 quantities at 19X4 prices.

Note: A common mistake by students is to add the prices and weights separately and multiply the totals, instead of multiplying each price by its weight and adding the products. In other words, $\sum p \times \sum q$ is calculated instead of $\sum (p \times q)$. This is quite wrong.

Answer 3

Laspeyre quantity index for year two with year one as base $= \dfrac{\sum q_2 p_1}{\sum q_1 p_1} \times 100$

Laspeyre quantity index for year three with year one as base $= \dfrac{\sum q_3 p_1}{\sum q_1 p_1} \times 100$

From the prices and quantities provided:

$q_1 p_1$	$q_2 p_1$	$q_3 p_1$
12	14	20
8	28	32
48	12	36
72	112	32
140	166	120

Laspeyre quantity index for year two $= \dfrac{166}{140} \times 100$

   $= 118.6$

Laspeyre quantity index for year three $= \dfrac{120}{140} \times 100$

   $= 85.7$

Answer 4

Year	Sales	Fixed base index (19X1 = 100)	Chain base index	
19X1	£1,000	100		100
19X2	£1,100	110.0	$\dfrac{110}{100} \times 100$	110
19X3	£1,210	121.0	$\dfrac{121}{110} \times 100$	110
19X4	£1,331	133.1	$\dfrac{133.1}{121} \times 100$	110
19X5	£1,464	146.4	$\dfrac{146.4}{133.1} \times 100$	110

Note: Chain base index for year n = $\dfrac{\text{Fixed base index for year n}}{\text{Fixed base index for previous year}} \times 100$

Although the sales of radios have increased each year, the chain base index numbers have remained static at 110. Therefore, the annual rate of increase of sales of radios is remaining constant rather than increasing. Do not confuse *rate* of increase with *actual* increase. Actual sales are increasing each year but the rate of increase is constant at 10% per year.

Answer 5

Tutorial note: A chain index expresses each index number as a percentage of the index number for the previous period.

Year	Calculation	Chain index
19X4		108.5
19X5	$\frac{134.8}{108.5} \times 100$	124.2
19X6	$\frac{157.1}{134.8} \times 100$	116.5
19X7	$\frac{182.0}{157.1} \times 100$	115.8
19X8	$\frac{197.1}{182.0} \times 100$	108.3
19X9	$\frac{223.5}{197.1} \times 100$	113.4
19Y0	$\frac{263.7}{223.5} \times 100$	118.0
19Y1	$\frac{295.0}{263.7} \times 100$	111.9
19Y2	$\frac{320.4}{295.0} \times 100$	108.6
19Y3	$\frac{335.1}{320.4} \times 100$	104.6
19Y4	$\frac{351.8}{335.1} \times 100$	105.0
19Y5	$\frac{373.2}{351.8} \times 100$	106.1

Answer 6

(a)

Commodity	Price	w	Price × w
A	110	10	1,100
B	98	5	490
C	136	3	408
D	125	2	250
		20	2,248

$\therefore$ Index number $= \frac{2,248}{20} = 112.4$

(b)

Commodity	Price	w	Price × w
A	110	90	9,900
B	98	5	490
C	136	3	408
D	125	2	250
		100	11,048

$$\therefore \text{ Index number} = \frac{11{,}048}{100} = 110.5$$

Answer 7

Biffo obviously has base year 19X4 since the index equals 100 in this year so it is necessary to adjust the figures for *Woof-Woof* by dividing each number by 250 – the 19X4 index, and multiplying by 100.

	19X2	*19X3*	*19X4*	*19X5*	*19X6*
Biffo	61	88	100	135	165
Woof-Woof	$\frac{210}{250} \times 100$	$\frac{230}{250} \times 100$	$\frac{250}{250} \times 100$	$\frac{300}{250} \times 100$	$\frac{360}{250} \times 100$
(Adjusted)	= 84	= 92	= 100	= 120	= 144

Both sets of figures now use 19X4 as base year and so can be directly compared.

Answer 8

Year	Calculation	Index (19Y0 = 100)
19X4	$\dfrac{108.5}{263.7} \times 100$	41.1
19X5	$\dfrac{134.8}{263.7} \times 100$	51.1
19X6	$\dfrac{157.1}{263.7} \times 100$	59.6
19X7	$\dfrac{182.0}{263.7} \times 100$	69.0
19X8	$\dfrac{197.1}{263.7} \times 100$	74.7
19X9	$\dfrac{223.5}{263.7} \times 100$	84.8
19Y0	$\dfrac{263.7}{263.7} \times 100$	100.0
19Y1	$\dfrac{295.0}{263.7} \times 100$	111.9
19Y2	$\dfrac{320.4}{263.7} \times 100$	121.5
19Y3	$\dfrac{335.1}{263.7} \times 100$	127.1
19Y4	$\dfrac{351.8}{263.7} \times 100$	133.4
19Y5	$\dfrac{373.2}{263.7} \times 100$	141.5

Answer 9

Taking 19X0 as the base year, calculate index numbers for prices and quantities for each of the items separately for year 19X1 for the following data and comment on the results.

Item	p_0	q_0	p_1	q_1
A	0.20	20	0.22	24
B	0.25	12	0.28	16
C	1.00	3	0.98	2

Item A   Price index $= \dfrac{0.22}{0.20} \times 100 = 110$

Quantity index $= \dfrac{24}{20} \times 100 = 120$

Item B	Price index	$= \dfrac{0.28}{0.25} \times 100$	$= 112$
	Quantity index	$= \dfrac{16}{12} \times 100$	$= 133$
Item C	Price index	$= \dfrac{0.98}{1.00} \times 100$	$= 98$
	Quantity index	$= \dfrac{2}{3} \times 100$	$= 67$

Comments

For items A, B and C price from 19X0 to 19X1 increased by 10%, 12% and a decrease of 2% respectively and quantities increased by 20%, 33% and decreased by 33% respectively.

Answer 10

(a)   **Base weighted index**

		19X5		19X7	
		Number	Wages	Number	Wages
		q_0	p_0	q_1	p_1
Administrative	Female	14	195	17	238
	Male	62	270	70	328
Clerical	Female	165	118	174	137
	Male	76	159	77	181
		317		338	

(i)   **All employees**

$p_0 q_0$	$p_1 q_0$
2,730	3,332
16,740	20,336
19,470	22,605
12,084	13,756
51,024	60,029

$$\text{Index (all employees)} = \frac{60,029}{51,024} \times 100 = 117.6$$

(ii)   **Male employees**

$p_0 q_0$	$p_1 q_0$
16,740	20,336
12,084	13,756
28,824	34,092

$$\text{Index (male employees)} = \frac{34,092}{28,824} \times 100 = 118.3$$

(iii)   **Administrative employees**

$p_0 q_0$	$p_1 q_0$
2,730	3,332
16,740	20,336
───────	───────
19,470	23,668

$$\text{Index (administrative employees)} = \frac{23,668}{19,470} \times 100 = 121.6$$

(b)   **Wages of administrative and clerical workers**

Introduction

A comparison of wages of different types of workers is important to monitor the differentials between different grades and the implementation of equal opportunity policies.

Summary

This report compares the increase in wages in the period 19X5 to 19X7 for different grades of work and different sexes, based on information from the 'New Earnings Survey'.

Findings

Indices showing increase in wages between 19X5 and 19X7.

All employees	117.6
Male	118.3
Female	116.8
Administrative	121.6
Clerical	115.2

Conclusions

In the two-year period wages have gone up by an average of 17.6%. The largest increase has occurred in the wages of administrators where wages have increased by 21.6%, women administrators having seen a 22% increase.

Males' wages overall have shown an increase of 18.3%, only marginally above the average rate of 17.6%.

Probably due to the increased responsibility of administrators in this more technological age, the wages of administrators have risen above the average level in response to the economics of supply and demand.

Answer 11

Index numbers have been obtained for each of the 10 main sections given and it is now necessary to combine these using the weights in order to calculate the index of retail prices.

Item	Index	Weight	Index × Weight
Food	123	299	36,777
Alcoholic drink	127	72	9,144
Tobacco	125	76	9,500
Fuel and light	134	71	9,514
Durables	113	67	7,571
Clothing and footwear	113	102	11,526
Transport	119	136	16,184
Miscellaneous	125	68	8,500
Services	132	63	8,316
Meals out	127	46	5,842
		1,000	122,874

$$\text{Index} = \frac{122,874}{1,000} = 122.874 = 123$$

So prices have risen by 23% between January 19X2 and 19X8.

Answer 12

Tutorial note: The combined index is obtained by multiplying each individual index by its weight, adding the results and dividing the total by the sum of the weights. Set the calculation out in vertical columns

Industry	Weight	Index	Index × Weight
A	41	35.6	1,459.6
B	123	154.7	19,028.1
C	15	99.3	1,489.5
D	85	98.6	8,381.0
	264		30,358.2
E	25	108.0	2,700.0
F	41	92.1	3,776.1
G	68	118.9	8,085.2
H	325	101.2	32,890.0
I	99	101.3	10,028.7
J	52	97.9	5,090.8
K	68	95.6	6,500.8
L	58	94.1	5,457.8
	736		74,529.4
	1,000		104,887.6

(a)   Index number for all industries $= \dfrac{104{,}887.6}{1{,}000} = 104.9$

(b)   Index number for A to D $= \dfrac{30{,}358.2}{264} = 115.0$

CHAPTER 7

ANSWERS

MAIN TYPES OF
PERFORMANCE INDICATORS

Answer 1

			19X3	*19X2*
(a)	(i)	Net profit on sales	$\dfrac{35,000}{200,000} \times 100$	$\dfrac{30,000}{120,000} \times 100$
			$= 17.5\%$	$= 25\%$
	(ii)	Gross profit on sales	$\dfrac{50,000}{200,000} \times 100$	$\dfrac{40,000}{120,000} \times 100$
			$= 25\%$	$= 33.3\%$
	(iii)	Return on capital employed	$\dfrac{35,000}{41,000} \times 100$	$\dfrac{30,000}{29,000} \times 100$
			$= 85.4\%$	$= 103.4\%$
	(iv)	Debtor collection period	$\dfrac{36,000}{200,000} \times 365$	$\dfrac{12,000}{120,000} \times 365$
			$= 66$ days	$= 37$ days
	(v)	Current ratio	$\dfrac{54,000}{25,000}$	$\dfrac{20,000}{6,000}$
			$= 2.2$	$= 3.3$
	(vi)	Acid test (or quick) ratio	$\dfrac{54,000 - 18,000}{25,000}$	$\dfrac{20,000 - 7,000}{6,000}$
			$= 1.4$	$= 2.2$

(b)   It is suggested that as an apparent result of a reduction in Free's selling prices during 19X2/X3, the following points could be made:

(i)   Free's sales have increased by £80,000 (66.7%).

(ii)   His gross profit has increased by £10,000 (25%) and his net profit by £5,000 (16.7%). The net profit has probably been affected by an increase in fixed costs (up from £10,000 in 19X2 to £15,000 in 19X3) as a result of the increase in sales.

(iii)   As a result of the reduction in selling prices his gross profit margin has also fallen sharply – from 33.3% in 19X2 to 25% in 19X3. This is, of course, to be expected.

(iv)   Free's return on capital employed still remains remarkably high, falling from 103.4% in 19X2 to 85.4% in 19X3 but note that these returns have been calculated on year end balances. Since Free has also drawn substantially from the business (£13,000 in 19X2 but rising to £23,000 in 19X3), his capital employed at the end of the year appears correspondingly smaller.

(v)   He also seems to have encouraged a greater volume of sales by granting a much longer period of credit – up from an average of 37 days in 19X2 to an average of 66 days in 19X3.

Alternatively, it may be that Free has not been able to cope with the increase in sales and his debtor control system has broken down. Whatever the reason, it has helped to convert a favourable bank balance of £1,000 at the end of 19X2 to an overdrawn one of £10,000 at the end of 19X3.

(vi)   It would appear that Free's liquidity position in 19X3 as measured by both the current ratio (2.2) and the acid test (or quick) ratio (1.4) is satisfactory, although the situation has deteriorated since 19X2 when the ratios were 3.3 and 2.2 respectively. In fact, although Free is trading successfully and his profit margins are high, his cash flow is at a critical level. This is sometimes known as *over-trading*.

Free ought to insist that his trade debtors settle their debts much more quickly than they appear to have been doing in 19X3. Otherwise he may need to reduce his own cash drawings since these have helped to exacerbate the cash position during the current year.

Answer 2

(a)   **Gross profit percentage**

$$\frac{\text{Gross profit}}{\text{Sales}} \times 100 \qquad = \qquad \frac{50,000}{100,000} \times 100 \qquad = \qquad 50\%$$

(b)   **Net profit percentage**

$$\frac{\text{Net profit}}{\text{Sales}} \times 100 \qquad = \qquad \frac{25,000}{100,000} \times 100 \qquad = \qquad 25\%$$

(c)   **Return on capital employed**

$$\frac{\text{Net profit}}{\text{Capital}} \times 100 \qquad = \qquad \frac{25,000}{33,000} \times 100 \qquad = \qquad 75.8\%$$

(d)   **Stock turnover**

$$\frac{\text{Cost of goods sold}}{\text{Closing stock}} \qquad = \qquad \frac{50,000}{12,000} \qquad = \qquad 4.2$$

or

$$\frac{\text{Cost of goods sold}}{\text{Average stock}} \qquad = \qquad \frac{50,000}{(10,000 + 12,000) \div 2} \qquad = \qquad 4.5$$

(e)   **Debtor collection period**

$$\frac{\text{Trade debtors}}{\text{Credit sales}} \times 365 \qquad = \qquad \frac{7,000}{100,000} \times 365 \qquad = \qquad 26 \text{ days}$$

(f)   **Current ratio**

$$\frac{\text{Current assets}}{\text{Current liabilities}} \qquad = \qquad \frac{20,000}{5,000} \qquad = \qquad 4$$

(g)   **Quick (or acid test) ratio**

$$\frac{\text{Current assets} - \text{Stocks}}{\text{Current liabilities}} = \frac{20,000 - 12,000}{5,000} = 1.6$$

Answer 3

Nothing can be said on economy as the inputs have only been given in terms of employees' time. Key information here would be the amount of raw materials used compared to the amount expected to be used.

The company has not been effective in its task as not all the output was produced. This may not be the fault of the operators – other factors such as machine breakdown may have caused this.

However, a measure of effectiveness could be stated as:

$$\frac{\text{Actual output}}{\text{Expected output}} \times 100 = \frac{49,000}{50,000} \times 100 = 98\% \text{ effective}$$

Efficiency of the operators can be measured against the standard set by the company.

The standard output for each input is one hour to produce one unit.

$$\frac{\text{Actual output}}{\text{Actual input}} = \frac{49,000 \text{ units}}{47,500 \text{ hours}} = 1.032 \text{ units per hour}$$

The employees therefore appear to have been efficient.

Answer 4

British Rail has been successful in increasing in real terms its receipts in relation to the distances covered. This does not mean that its total receipts have increased. The business may well have cut back on railway lines that were not economically viable.

It has not been successful in controlling its costs measured on the same basis as receipts and therefore the net effect of 41 and 42 is broadly neutral.

Productivity of staff has increased significantly. Items 43 and 45 both indicate this.

Wage costs are presumably a significant element of total costs. The relationship of sales revenue to wages costs has improved slightly.

Item 46 indicates that British Rail is using its track more efficiently or that it has removed lines which were uneconomic to run (ie. few trips were made on them). This is supporting evidence of the comments made on item 41.

Answer 5

(a)   **Room occupancy**

$$\frac{\text{Total number of rooms occupied}}{\text{Rooms available to be let}} = \frac{200 + 30}{240 + 40} = 82.1\%$$

(b)   Bed occupancy

$$\frac{\text{Total number of beds occupied}}{\text{Total number of beds available}} \quad = \quad \frac{6{,}450 \text{ guests} \times 2 \text{ days per guest}}{[(240 \times 2) + (40 \times 1)] \times 30 \text{ days}}$$

$$= \quad \frac{12{,}900}{15{,}600} \quad = \quad 82.7\%$$

(c)   Average guest rate

$$\frac{\text{Total revenue}}{\text{Number of guests}} \quad = \quad \frac{\pounds774{,}000}{6{,}450} \quad = \quad \pounds120$$

(d)   Revenue utilisation

$$\frac{\text{Actual revenue}}{\text{Maximum revenue from available rooms}} \quad = \quad \frac{\pounds774{,}000}{[(240 \times \pounds110) + (40 \times \pounds70)] \times 30 \text{ days}}$$

$$= \quad \frac{\pounds774{,}000}{\pounds876{,}000} \quad = \quad 88.4\%$$

(e)   Cost of cleaning supplies per occupied room per day

$$\frac{\pounds5{,}000}{(200 + 30) \times 30 \text{ days}} \quad = \quad \pounds0.7$$

(f)   Average cost per occupied bed

$$\frac{\text{Total cost}}{\text{Number of beds occupied}} \quad = \quad \frac{\pounds100{,}000 + \pounds5{,}000 + \pounds22{,}500}{6{,}450 \times 2} \quad = \quad \pounds9.9$$

CHAPTER 8

ANSWERS

WRITING REPORTS

Answer 1

Information	Source	Use
1 Wages analysed by type of employment	New Earnings Survey	Allows wages of car workers to be compared with those of workers in other sectors
2 Production of cars and commercial vehicles	Business Monitor 'Cars and Commercial Vehicles'	Enables comparison of changes in volume of output to be made
3 Index of retail prices	Employment Gazette	Enables a comparison to be made of increases in wages in the industry with increases in the cost of living

Answer 2

The systematic or schematic presentation of a report demonstrates that the person who has written it has tackled the work involved in some organised and logical way and enables the reader to assimilate and comprehend the contents of the report quickly.

A specially commissioned report on, for example, market trends or accidents in the work place might begin with an *Introduction* under which the circumstances leading to the commissioning of the report are described, the background established.

It will certainly have a section headed *Terms of reference* which defines the job that was given to the person or group responsible for preparing the report, ie. the purpose of the report.

It is usual for the writer of a report to explain in a section headed *Procedure* how the investigation or survey on which the report is based was conducted – how information was obtained, analysed and so on.

What has been discovered is then stated under *Findings*. In this section the information is classified and its apparent meanings and implications explained. A succinct synopsis of the findings is usually presented as *Conclusions*.

A specially commissioned report normally ends with *Recommendations* which are essentially the author's view of the findings, and a clear statement of what can and needs to be done.

Answer 3

Procedure for selection of pupils for college scholarships

Introduction

This report has been produced at the request of Mr X to clarify the current procedure.

Summary

The report describes the procedure adopted by the Education Authority for the selection of pupils for college scholarships.

Procedure

There are two types of potential candidates:

(1)   Those who enter for the February examination and pass it.
(2)   Those who are 'borderline cases'.

In the case of (1), a letter is sent confirming acceptance as a result of the examination entry.

In the case of (2), the following sequence is adopted:

(a)   Special panels of the Education Committee visit schools to discuss each case with the Head, review schoolwork and interview individuals.

(b)   After 14 days, the school Head will notify parents either that their children have not been selected, or will be considered further.

(c)   Parents of children for further consideration receive a Form B81 for completion and return to the Head.

(d)   By the end of July, parents will receive the result and, if their children have been selected, the name of the college offering a place will be given.

Conclusion and recommendations

The selection procedure inevitably takes time and it would be helpful if parents were told about this to avoid unnecessary anxiety and fruitless enquiries.

Signed ....

CHAPTER 9

ANSWERS

ORGANISATIONS - STRUCTURE AND PERFORMANCE

Answer 1

There are four main methods of classifying organisations:

(a)   **By legal structure** – This distinguishes between organisations that are sole traders/partnerships, limited companies or government bodies.

(b)   **By profit objective** – This distinguishes organisations that have profit as an important objective and those whose objectives are to provide cost efficient services.

(c)   **By Answer** – This distinguishes manufacturers, wholesalers, retailers and service organisations.

(d)   **By size** – This distinguishes organisations which have a single unit from national and multi-national organisations.

Answer 2

Specific order costing is the costing method used when goods or services are provided which are specific to the needs of the customer.

Specific order costing methods include job costing and contract costing. Job costing is used when the work is expected to be completed within a short timescale. Contract costing is used for larger works, eg. building tunnels, bridges, motorways.

Answer 3

Costs may be classified in many different ways according to the purpose of the information to be provided. Costs are often classified:

(a)   **By product** – This is to enable product costs to be determined and is used when valuing stocks, measuring profits and may also be useful when setting selling prices.

(b)   **For decision making** – This is to enable managers to know which costs are affected by a particular decision. This is also known as the distinction between relevant and irrelevant costs which is often the same as the classification of costs between those that remain constant in total (fixed costs) and those whose total changes when Answer changes (variable costs).

Answer 4

Quantitative performance measures are those which can be expressed in numerical terms, eg. cost per unit, ratios.

Qualitative performance measures are opinions, often based on questionnaires.

CHAPTER 10

ANSWERS

REPORTING

Answer 1

Strategic management require summarised information which may be supported by more detailed analysis.

Tactical management require departmental/functional information which may be quite detailed.

Operational management require very detailed short-term information.

Answer 2

Reliability
Completeness
Relevance
Objectivity
Comparability
Timeliness
Understandability

Answer 3

Filing of annual accounts at Companies House
Statistical returns to Government agencies
Value added tax to Customs & Excise
Corporation tax returns to Inland Revenue

ANSWERS

UNIT 8

PREPARING VAT RETURNS

CHAPTER 1

ANSWERS

INTRODUCTION TO VAT - SUPPLIES AND REGISTRATION

1   Answer

			£
(a)	Net price		216.00
	VAT £216 × 17.5%		37.80
	Gross price		253.80
(b)	Net price		5,926.00
	VAT £5,926 × 17.5%		1,037.05
	Gross price		6,963.05
(c)	Net price		11,144.00
	VAT £11,144 × 17.5%		1,950.20
	Gross price		13,094.20

2   Answer

			£
(a)	Gross price		715.81
	VAT £715.81 × 7/47		106.61
	Net price		609.20

(Check £609.20 × 17.5% = £106.61)

(b)	Gross price		1,292.50
	VAT £1,292.50 × 7/47		192.50
	Net price		1,100.00

(Check £1,100 × 17.5% = £192.50)

(c)	Gross price		7,336.23
	VAT £7,336.23 × 7/47		1,092.63
	Net price		6,243.60

(Check £6,243.60 × 17.5% = £1,092.63)

3   Answer

Su Chin

	£
Purchase price	1,000
VAT (£1,000 × 17.5%)	175
Total price	1,175

	£
Selling price	3,000
VAT (£3,000 × 17.5%)	525
Total price	3,525

Therefore:

Input VAT	175
Output VAT	525
VAT due to Customs & Excise	350

This £350 is the VAT at 17.5% on the value added by Su Chin, (£3,000 - £1,000) × 17.5%.

Jake

	£
Purchase price	3,000
VAT (£3,000 × 17.5%)	525
Total price	3,525

	£
Selling price	6,000
VAT (£6,000 × 17.5%)	1,050
Total price	7,050

Therefore:

Input VAT	525
Output VAT	1,050
VAT due to Customs & Excise	525

This £525 is the VAT at 17.5% on the value added by Jake, (£6,000 − £3,000) × 17.5%.

Consumer

	£
Purchase price	6,000
VAT (£6,000 × 17.5%)	1,050
Total price	7,050

As the consumer does not resell the cello then there is no output tax on which to set off the input tax of £1,050 that has been incurred. The consumer must bear the full cost of the VAT.

The VAT of £1,050 borne by the consumer has been accounted for to HM Customs & Excise in stages, as follows:

	Net Price £	*Tax* £
By the wood producer: Wood	1,000	175
By Su Chin Value added	2,000	350
	3,000	525
By Jake Value added	3,000	525
	6,000	1,050

4   Answer

	£
VAT on purchase (£1,762.50 × 17.5/117.5)	262.50
VAT on sale (£2,000 × 17.5%)	350.00
VAT paid to Customs & Excise	87.50

5   Answer

(a)   Exempt.
(b)   Taxable.
(c)   Exempt.
(d)   Taxable.
(e)   Taxable.
(f)   Exempt.
(g)   Exempt.
(h)   Taxable.
(i)   Taxable.

6   Answer

(a)   Standard rated.
(b)   Zero rated.
(c)   Standard rated.
(d)   Standard rated.
(e)   Exempt.
(f)   Standard rated.
(g)   Zero rated.
(h)   Standard rated.
(i)   Standard rated.

7   Answer

(a)   The gift will not be treated as a supply as it cost less than £15.

(b)   The gift of the gold watch will be treated as a supply. The value of the supply will be the cost of the watch, £280.

(c)   The samples will not be treated as supplies, as only one sample was given to each person.

(d)   The meal pack is a mixed supply. The sandwich is zero rated, whilst the packet of crisps and the chocolate bar are standard rated.

(e)   The book and bookmark are treated as a composite supply, and will be zero rated.

8   Answer

(a)   The supply of the book and discs is a mixed supply, and the selling price must be apportioned to calculate the VAT.

(i)   Apportionment on basis of values of supplies:

	£
Value of book	50
Value of discs	25
	75
VAT on book - zero rated £50 @ 0%	-
VAT on discs - standard rated £25 @ 17.5%	4.37
Total VAT	4.37

(ii)   Apportionment on basis of cost of supplies:

	£
Cost of book	10
Cost of discs	8
	18
VAT on book - zero rated $10/18 \times £75$ @ 0%	-
VAT on discs - standard rated $8/18 \times £75$ @ 17.5%	5.83
Total VAT	5.83

(b)   The supply of the book in a presentation case is a composite supply, and will be treated as a single zero rated supply.

9   Answer

     (a)   Jones, in respect of his carpentry business. His stamp collecting hobby is not included in the registration.

     (b)   (i)   Mary and Jane, in respect of their catering business.

                (ii)   Jane in respect of her hairdressing business.

     (c)   (i)   Donald and Douglas, one registration for both the photography business and the antique shop.

                (ii)   Donald and Dora, in respect of the guest house.

                (iii)   Dora, in respect of the beauty salon.

     (d)   (i)   Slick Slacks Ltd, the clothing shop.

                (ii)   Sally Steel, in respect of the interior design consultancy.

CHAPTER 2

ANSWERS

VAT INVOICES, VAT PERIODS, RECORDS REQUIRED

1   Answer

(a)   The invoice has no identifying number.

(b)   The invoice does not bear the VAT registration number of XYZ Ltd.

(c)   There is no description of the goods.

(d)   The VAT has been incorrectly calculated. A maximum cash discount of 3% is offered for payment within 10 days therefore the VAT should be calculated on £2,160 net of this cash discount whether or not it is taken. The correct amount of VAT is therefore 17.5% × £2,160.00 – (3% × £2,160.00) = £366.67.

2   Answer

(a)   The invoice does not show the time of supply.

(b)   The invoice does not describe the goods or services.

(c)   the invoice has not been completed to show the rate of VAT.

3   Answer

	Net	VAT @ 17.5%	Gross
	£	£	£
(a)	200.00	35.00	235.00
(b)	480.00	84.00	564.00
(c)	1,300.00	227.50	1,527.50
(d)	2,360.00	413.00	2,773.00
(e)	4,444.00	777.70	5,221.70
(f)	8,080.00	1,414.00	9,494.00

4   Answer

	Net	VAT @ 17.5%	Gross
	£	£	£
(a)	580.00	101.50	681.50
(b)	900.00	157.50	1,057.50
(c)	1,280.00	224.00	1,504.00
(d)	4,140.00	724.50	4,864.50
(e)	6,680.00	1,169.00	7,849.00
(f)	9,120.00	1,596.00	10,716.00

5   Answer

	Gross	VAT @ 7/47	Net
	£	£	£
(a)	117.03	17.43	99.60
(b)	991.70	147.70	844.00
(c)	1,238.45	184.45	1,054.00
(d)	4,761.57	709.17	4,052.40
(e)	7,153.87	1,065.47	6,088.40
(f)	9,973.40	1,485.40	8,488.00

6   **Answer**

(a)   Per unit

(i)   Rounding to the nearest 0.1p

VAT on each size 1 widget	=	£1.17 × 17.5%
	=	20.47p
Rounded to	=	20.5p
VAT on each size 2 widget	=	£1.59 × 17.5%
	=	27.82p
Rounded to	=	27.8p

Total VAT
(25 × 20.5p) + (35 × 27.8p)   =   £14.855

Rounded to   £14.85

(ii)   Rounding to the nearest 0.5p

VAT on each size 1 widget	=	£1.17 × 17.5%
	=	20.47p
Rounded to	=	20.5p
VAT on each size 2 widget	=	£1.59 × 17.5%
	=	27.82p
Rounded to	=	28.0p

Total VAT
(25 × 20.5p) + (35 ×28.0p)   =   £14.925

Rounded to   £14.92

(b)   Per line

(i)   Rounding to the nearest 0.1p

Net price of 25 widgets 25 × £1.17	=	£29.25
VAT on 25 size 1 widgets	=	£29.25 ×17.5%
	=	511.87p
Rounded to	=	511.9p
Net price of 35 widgets 35 × £1.59	=	£55.65
VAT on 35 size 2 widgets	=	£55.65 × 17.5%
	–	973.87p
Rounded to	=	973.9p

Total VAT (511.9p + 973.9p)   =   £14.858

Rounded to   £14.85

(ii)   Rounding to the nearest 0.5p

Net price of 25 widgets 25 × £1.17		=	£29.25
VAT on 25 size 1 widgets		=	£29.25 ×17.5%
		=	511.87p
Rounded to		=	512.0p
Net price of 35 widgets 35 ×£1.59		=	£55.65
VAT on 35 size 2 widgets		=	£55.65 × 17.5%
		=	973.87p
Rounded to		=	974.0p

Total VAT (512.0p + 974.0p)   £14.86

7   Answer

	£
Net price of goods	1,000.00
VAT ((£1,000 − £30) × 17.5%)	169.75
	1,169.75

The VAT is calculated on the net price of the goods assuming that the highest cash discount offered is taken up. The VAT does not alter even if the cash discount is not taken up.

8   Answer

The VAT charged on the supplies is calculated on the assumption that the 5% cash discount will be taken. Using the method of rounding each line on the invoice to the nearest 0.5p the VAT charged is:

	Amount liable to VAT £	VAT @ 17.5% £
5 crates 5 × £10.05 = £50.25 less 5%	47.74	8.355
8 tubs 8 × £13.25 = £106 less 5%	100.70	17.620
6 barrels 6 × £15.15= £90.90 less 5%	86.35	15.110
		41.085

Total VAT charged on the invoice (rounding down)   £41.08

9   Answer

(a)   Giles should apply to have prescribed accounting periods ending 5 January, 5 April, 5 July and 5 October.

(b)   Giles should apply to have monthly prescribed accounting periods.

10   **Answer**

He must furnish a return no later than 28 February 1998. Payments are made as follows:

		£
Year to 31 December 1997		
Quarterly payments commencing 30 April 1997	3 @ £720	2,160
Final payment no later than 28 February 1998	£(3,820 – 2,160)	1,660
		3,820
Year to 31 December 1998		
Quarterly payments commencing 30 April 1998		
3 @ £(3,820 × 20%) = 3 @ £764		2,292

11   **Answer**

Larry's records are not adequate for the following reasons:

(a)   The records of outputs should:

   (i)   be in the same order as the invoices ie, in order of issue not payment, and

   (ii)   include the VAT exclusive amount of the supplies.

(b)   The invoices for supplies received should be filed in such a way that they can easily be referred to.

(c)   The records of inputs should:

   (i)   be in such an order as is possible to easily locate the supporting invoice; and

   (ii)   include the VAT exclusive amount of the inputs.

(d)   The VAT account must be kept up to date for each VAT period.

CHAPTER 3

ANSWERS

COMPLETING THE VAT RETURN

1 **Answer**

    (a)   **Invoice No 001**

        The VAT shown on the invoice is too low. Michael should either:

        (i)   account for VAT of $\frac{7}{47} \times$ £2,300 =   £342.55
              and adjust the net output to   £1,957.45

              or

        (ii)   issue an additional invoice for   £50.00
              account for VAT of   £350.00
              leaving the net output at   £2,000.00

    (b)   **Invoice No 002**

        The VAT shown on the invoice is too high. Michael should either:

        (i)   account for VAT of   £400.00
              and leave the net output at   £2,000.00

              or

        (ii)   issue a credit note for   £50.00
              account for VAT of   £350.00
              leaving the net output at   £2,000.00

2 **Answer**

		£	£
(a)	**Outputs**		
	Sales day book		
	Mar sales	23,000	
	Apr sales	21,000	
	May sales	22,000	
	Furniture	2,000	
		———	
			68,000
	Cash receipts book		
	Mar sales	2,000	
	Apr sales	1,000	
	May sales	2,000	
		———	
			5,000
	Total outputs		73,000

(b)   **Output tax**

		£	£
Sales day book			
	Mar	4,025	
	Apr	3,675	
	May	4,200	
		———	
			11,900
Cash receipts book			
	Mar	350	
	Apr	175	
	May	350	
		———	
			875
			———
Total output tax			12,775
			———

(c)   **Inputs**

			£	£
Purchases day book				
	Mar	purchases	16,000	
		expenses	2,000	
	Apr	purchases	14,000	
		expenses	3,000	
	May	purchases	14,000	
		expenses	2,000	
			———	
				51,000
Cash payments book				
	Mar	purchases	1,600	
	Apr	purchases	2,400	
	May	purchases	2,000	
			———	
				6,000
				———
Total inputs				57,000
				———

(d)   **Input tax**

		£	£
Purchases day book			
	Mar	3,150	
	Apr	2,975	
	May	2,800	
		———	
			8,925
Cash payments book			
	Mar	280	
	Apr	420	
	May	350	
		———	
			1,050
			———
Total input tax			9,975
			———

3   Answer

Summary of outputs

	Gross £	VAT £	Net £	Discount £
1	2,332.50	332.50	2,000	100
2	4,198.50	598.50	3,600	180
3	4,665.00	665.00	4,000	200
4	6,997.50	997.50	6,000	300
5	11,662.50	1,662.50	10,000	500
	29,856.00	4,256.00	25,600	1,280

Summary of inputs

	Gross £	VAT £	Net £
Less detailed	1,880.00	280.00	1,600
Invoice	11,750.00	1,750.00	10,000
	13,630.00	2,030.00	11,600

Value Added Tax Return

For the period

For Official Use

HM Customs and Excise

Registration number

Period

You could be liable to a financial penalty if your completed return and all the VAT payable are not received by the due date.

Due date:

For Official Use

Your VAT Office telehpone number is

ATTENTION

If you are using Retail Scheme B1, D or J, please remember to carry out your annual adjustment at the appropriate time.

Before you fill in this form please read the notes on the back and the VAT leaflet 'Filling in your VAT return'. Fill in all boxes clearly in ink, and write 'none' where necessary. Don't put a dash or leave any box blank. If there are no pence write "00" in the pence column. Do not enter more than one amount in any box.

For official use				
	VAT due in this period on sales and other outputs	1	4256	00
	VAT due in this period on acquisitions from other EC Member States	2	NONE	
	Total VAT due (the sum of boxes 1 and 2)	3	4256	00
	VAT reclaimed in this period on purchases and other inputs (including acquisitions from the EC)	4	2030	00
	Net VAT to be paid to Customs or reclaimed by you (Difference between boxes 3 and 4)	5	2226	00
	Total value of sales and all other outputs excluding any VAT, include your box 8 figure	6	25,600	00
	Total value of purchases and all other inputs excluding any VAT, include your box 9 figure	7	11,600	00
	Total value of all supplies of goods and related services, excluding any VAT, to other EC Member States	8	NONE	00
	Total value of all acquisitions of goods and related services, excluding any VAT, from other EC Member States	9	NONE	00

Retail schemes.   If you have used any of the schemes in the period covered by this return, enter the relevant letter(s) in this box.

If you are enclosing a payment please tick this box.

DECLARATION: You, or someone on your behalf, must sign below.

I __ ___ ___ ___ ___ ___ ___ ___ ___ ___ declare that the
(Full name of signatory in BLOCK LETTERS)
information given above is true and complete.

Signature __ ___ ___ ___ ___ ___ Date __ _____ 19 __ ___

A false declaration can result in prosecution.

CD 2859/N3(08/93)   F3790 (February 1994)

VAT 100

CHAPTER 4

ANSWERS

SPECIAL CASES

1   Answer

(a)   **Outputs**

Date	VAT £	Net £
3.6.96	245	1,400
21.6.96	175	1,000
11.7.96	350	2,000
23.8.96	280	1,600
29.8.96	385	2,200
	1,435	8,200

(b)   **Inputs**

Date	VAT £	Net £
29.6.96	105	600
29.6.96	140	800
30.7.96	175	1,000
30.7.96	525	3,000
29.8.96	105	600
	1,050	6,000

2   Answer

The payment of £6,700 will be allocated as to:

	£
1.1.97	4,700
21.1.97	2,000
	6,700

Bad debt relief will be given for £875 as follows:

	Gross £	VAT £
21.1.97	3,000	
12.2.97	2,350	350
11.3.97	3,525	525
		875

Bad debt relief of £350 can be claimed on 12 August 1997 and £525 on 11 September 1997, so the relief should be claimed on the return for the quarter ended 30 September 1997 as input tax.

3   **Answer**

VAT on the cost of the car £24,000 × 17.5% = £4,200.
This is not recoverable.

VAT on the compact disc player £470 × 17.5/117.5 = £70.
This is not recoverable as it was installed at the time of purchase of the car.

VAT on the telephone £235 × 17.5/117.5 = £35.
This is recoverable as it is for business use and was supplied after the original purchase.

If the cost of the compact disc player and the telephone are to be capitalised then the car will appear in the accounts at the following value:

	£
Original cost	24,000
VAT on cost	4,200
Compact disc player (including VAT)	470
Telephone (excluding VAT)	200
	28,870

CHAPTER 5

ANSWERS

ADMINISTRATION

1   Answer

Since this is a query about output tax, the solution should be found in section III of the VAT Guide.

Delivery charges (postage and packing) etc

If, when you supply goods, you make an arrangement to deliver or post them for an extra charge, the extra charge is for the supply of a separate delivery service. If you send goods by post, the charge made to you by the Post Office is exempt, but your charge to your customer is taxable even if it is exactly equal to the charge made to you by the Post Office. Your supply of delivery services is standard-rated if the goods are sent to an address in the UK and zero-rated if they are sent elsewhere.

However, if the terms of your agreement with your customer for the supply of the goods requires you to deliver or post them to him, there is no separate supply of delivery or postage. This applies even if you show a separate charge. This means that you make a single supply of delivered goods and if the supply of the goods is zero-rated then the zero rating also covers the delivery or postage. This applies to most mail order transactions, but not if a delivery service is available at an extra charge for customers who request it.

Applying this guidance to Jack's case, the solution is:

(a)   If the arrangement to post the goods is a one-off arrangement, then the charge for postage and packing is standard rated.

(b)   If delivery is part of Jack's normal terms of sale, the charge will be zero rated as there will be a single supply of goods and delivery.

2   Answer

Changes requiring amendment of registration

Any of the following changes require your registration to be amended:

(a)   a change in the name or trading name of the business, or the name and/or address of any partner in the business;

(b)   a change in the composition of a partnership, but one or more of the former partners remains in the partnership;

(c)   a change in the address of the principal place at which the business is carried on;

(d)   a change in the trade classification of the business;

(e)   a change in bank account number, bank sorting code or Girobank account number.

You must notify your local VAT office in writing within 30 days of the above changes, quoting your registration number and giving the date on which the charge took place. Your registration number will not be altered as a result of these changes.

Robert and Richard must notify the local VAT office because:
(a)   there has been a change in the trading name, and
(b)   there has been a change in the composition of the partnership.

The changes should be notified by 3 March 1997.

PRACTICE DEVOLVED

ASSESSMENTS

ANSWERS

UNIT 7

PRACTICE DEVOLVED ASSESSMENT 1

ANSWERS

EDWARDS ELECTRONICS LTD

Task 1

The condition and performance ratios are presented in the pro forma company analysis sheets as follows:

Liquidity/Cashflow indicators			
Financial year	*19X0*	*19X1*	*19X2*
Current ratio: [Current assets: Current liabilities]	1.61:1	2.02:1	2.54:1
Acid test ratio: [Current assets – Stocks: Current liabilities]	1.01:1	1.20:1	1.45:1
Cash ratio: [Cash: Current liabilities]	0.35 : 1	0.38 : 1	0.39 : 1

Performance indicators			
Financial year	*19X0*	*19X1*	*19X2*
Return on capital employed (ROCE)			
[Net profit/Owners investment × 100 (%)]	4.71%	5.15%	10.44%
Net profit margin			
[Net profit/Sales × 100 (%)]	2.75%	3.31%	6.62%
Asset efficiency/Turnover			
[Sales/Net total assets]	1.71 times	1.56 times	1.58 times
Gross profit margin			
[Gross profit/Sales × 100 (%)]	46.28%	44.44%	45.28%
Expense: Sales ratios			
Admin. expenses: Sales	32.09%	31.30%	29.63%
Distribution costs: Sales	10.84%	10.12%	10.07%
Interest costs: Sales	1.69%	1.65%	2.76%
[All measured as % figures]			
Fixed asset efficiency/Turnover			
[Sales/Fixed assets]	2.24 times	2.23 times	2.24 times
Stock turnover			
[Cost of sales: Average stock]	3.11	3.10	2.82
Debtor turnover			
[Sales: Debtors]	5.16	5.16	5.03
Debtor payment period			
[Debtors/Sales × 365]	70.7 days	70.7 days	72.6 days
Creditor turnover			
[Purchases: Creditors]	2.28	3.03	4.0
Creditor payment period			
[Creditors/Purchases × 365]	160.1 days	120.6 days	91.3 days

WORKINGS

All figures are directly worked using figures for the balances suggested in the pro forma document.

Note that:

– Owners investment for ROCE is measured as capital plus retained profits at the end of each year. Thus 19X0 ROCE is measured as $11.1 \div 235.7 = 4.71\%$ and so forth for later years.

– Net profit is taken as the net profit referred to in the profit and loss statements – ie, before taxation.

– Stock turnover is computed as suggested. For 19X0 we have:

    Cost of sales = £216,600

    Average stock = (£68,300 + £71,000) ÷ 2 = £69,650

    Thus stock turnover = £216,600 ÷ £69,650 = 3.11

Similar calculations apply for other years.

– As specific debtor figures are not given for each year, the figure taken for debtor calculations is that of 'debtors and prepayments' (being the closest approximation to debtor figures).

– Trade creditor figures have been used to assess creditor turnover and creditor periods.

Tutorial note: the figures to use in the ratios have been quite clearly specified in the pro forma. However, any reasonable variations around the points made in the above notes would be accepted.

Gearing indicators			
Financial year	*19X0*	*19X1*	*19X2*
Gearing ratio: [Interest-bearing debt: Owners investment]	7.3%	6.8%	16.0%
Leverage: [All creditor funding: Owners investment]	57.5%	43.2%	45.6%

Interest cover:
    [Profits before interest: Interest incurred
    (per P/L)]
	2.6	3.0	3.4

Gearing and leverage are given as percentages; this reflects the usual expression of such figures.

Figures for leverage include 'all creditor funding' equal to all loans and current liabilities.

Task 2

Suggested responses to Jeff's comments are as follows

> The inflation indices given in my earlier note indicate an inflation rate of 6%
> annually over 19X1 and 19X2.

Comment

Yes they do. The indices reflect a year-on-year 6% increase, ie:

- For 19X0/X1, the index increase is $(118.72 - 112.00) \div 112.00 = 0.06$ or 6%
- For 19X1/X2, the index increase is $(125.84 - 118.72) \div 118.72 = 0.06$ or 6%

> The sales position is not healthy. Sales revenues have been growing and sales
> prices have been increasing roughly in line with inflation rates. However,
> inflation-adjusted 19X2 and 19X3 sales revenue figures to 19X1 price levels
> indicate that sales volumes have been falling.

Comment

Yes, this is true; note that:

- 19X0 sales value is £403,200

- 19X1 sales value adjusted to 19X0 price levels is $£423,000 \times \dfrac{112.0}{118.72} = £399,057$

- 19X2 sales value adjusted to 19X0 price levels is $£442,800 \times \dfrac{112.0}{125.84} = £394,100$

Sales value in real terms and sales volumes are falling.

> The improved company performance over the three year period is largely a product
> of highly-effective cost control as indicated by cost of sales: sales and
> expenses: sales ratios.

Comment

All the cost ratios mentioned were calculated in Task 1 excepting cost of sales:sales. This latter ratio is calculated as 53.72%, 55.56% and 54.72% for the three years respectively.

All expenses:sales ratios (excepting interest cost:sales) have shown improvement over the three-year period. However, cost of sales:sales has shown some deterioration. There seems to be evidence of some control of general expenses/costs but not necessarily of cost of sales.

The reduction in expenses:sales figures have been responsible for some overall increase in net profit margins which, given increases in sales values, have resulted in good increases in net profits. However, another big contributor appears to have been 'other income' which accounts for £12,400 (£16,800 − £4,400) of the net profit increase of £29,300 − £11,100 = £18,200.

The statement is partly true. Control of general expenses and 'other income' seems largely responsible for improved performance.

The balance sheet figures show outstanding debt liabilities at the end of each year. These figures are not reflective/representative of the average amount of debt outstanding over the whole of each respective year.

Using the figures for the average interest rate charged to us annually and our annual interest charges in the P/L (from the earlier statements), the average amounts of interest-bearing debt over each year have been £37,777, £36,842 and £97,600 respectively.

Comment

This is true. Balance sheet debt (at least as far as discernible from the figures given) has increased from £17,200 (19X0) to £18,600 (19X1) and £45,000 (19X2). Estimates of interest-bearing debt for each year are as follows:

- 19X0 $£6,800 \times \dfrac{100}{18} = £37,777$ (= Interest for year $\times \dfrac{100}{\text{Interest rate}}$)

- 19X1 $£7,000 \times \dfrac{100}{19} = £36,842$

- 19X2 $£12,200 \times \dfrac{100}{12.5} = £97,600$

These figures agree with those given.

The proportion of company profits taken up by taxation has increased over the three-year period.

Comment

True. The figures of taxation ÷ profits before taxation indicate proportionate tax liabilities as follows:

- 19X0 £3,900 ÷ £11,100 = 35.14%
- 19X1 £5,300 ÷ £14,000 = 37.86%
- 19X2 £11,700 ÷ £29,300 = 39.93%

These reflect proportionate increases over the three-year period.

Overall total profits have improved over the three-year period and the shareholders have benefited from the improvement. The company is in a healthier state generally.

Comment

Total profits have certainly increased over the period – from £7,200 (19X0) to £8,700 (19X1) and £17,600 (19X2). The shareholders have benefited from increased dividends which have gone up from £3,800 (19X0) to £4,500 (19X1) and £8,800 (19X2). These increases are of more than 6% (the inflation rate) and are therefore real increases. Retained profits have also increased progressively by more than the inflation rate. ROCE (before tax) has also increased (per earlier figures). If ROCE (after tax) figures were calculated, these would be found to be 3.05% (19X0), 3.2% (19X1) and 6.27% (19X2). The shareholders have therefore benefited according to these ROCE measures.

However, the company could not be said to be 'in a healthier state'. Sales volumes (the lifeblood of the company) are falling and the company seems highly dependent on 'other income'.

The position needs careful review. The trading problems must be addressed and resolved if the company is to have a healthy future.

Task 3

It is suggested that comment on the (other) main aspects of the corporate performance of Edwards Electronics Ltd over the past three years might be made as follows:

Edwards Electronics Ltd
Notes on corporate performance (19X0 – 19X2)

Performance as measured by ROCE (shareholders' funds) has improved over the three-year period as earlier identified.

ROCE of capital is measured as shareholders' funds plus long-term debt and returns are taken as being before tax. ROCE has improved from 4.39% [£11,100 ÷ (£235,700 + £17,200)] (19X0) to 4.82% (19X1) and 9.0% (19X2).

A major reason for the improvements in the ROCE figures is the improvement in net profit margins which have themselves largely resulted from improved figures for expenses:sales (possibly down to better cost control) and other incomes (which have grown substantially over the period). These points have already been made. Net profit margins have improved over the period notwithstanding a small decline in gross profit margins as a result of the factors identified.

ROCE has been adversely affected by reductions in total asset turnover figures which have reduced from 1.71 (19X0) to 1.58 (19X2). Fixed asset turnover/efficiency has remained almost constant, meaning that each £ of sales revenue each year has required roughly the same level of fixed asset investment. However, customer/debtor payment periods have slightly increased and (trade) creditor payment periods substantially decreased. Both have decreased net total asset turnover and, as a result, ROCE.

Stock turnover has also reduced with similar effect (on net total asset turnover and ROCE). This must cause concern, particularly in the light of declining sales volumes. Are there real problems in selling the company products?

Gearing has increased over the period from 7.3% (19X0) to 16.0% (19X2) (defined as interest-bearing debt:owner's investment). Average levels of annual debt have also increased (as earlier computed) from £37,777 (19X0) to £97,600 (19X2). However, financial risk still appears low – interest cover being more than 3.

Leverage shows a reduction but largely because of reduced trade and other creditor finance. So this is not a healthy sign.

All liquidity ratios (current, acid-test and cash) seem to have improved, largely as a result of less current creditor liabilities. There is therefore less liquidity risk.

Overall performance appears relatively healthy but major concerns are declining sales volumes, declining creditor periods and reduced debtor and stock turnovers. These problems must be addressed.

Task 4

Time series figures are as follows:

<table>
<tr><td colspan="5">TIME SERIES ANALYSIS
Figures in £'000</td></tr>
<tr>
<td>Time periods

19X0</td>
<td>Quarterly figures</td>
<td>4-quarterly moving average figures [Gen. trend]</td>
<td>4-quarterly moving average figures [Centred trend]</td>
<td>Seasonal effects [per quarter]</td>
</tr>
<tr><td>3 months to 31 March</td><td>78.8</td><td></td><td></td><td></td></tr>
<tr><td></td><td></td><td></td><td></td><td></td></tr>
<tr><td>3 months to 30 June</td><td>107.2</td><td></td><td></td><td></td></tr>
<tr><td></td><td></td><td>100.80</td><td></td><td></td></tr>
<tr><td>3 months to 30 September</td><td>85.9</td><td></td><td>101.525</td><td>(15.625)</td></tr>
<tr><td></td><td></td><td>102.25</td><td></td><td></td></tr>
<tr><td>3 months to 31 December</td><td>131.3</td><td></td><td>103.40</td><td>27.9</td></tr>
<tr><td>19X1</td><td></td><td>104.55</td><td></td><td></td></tr>
<tr><td>3 months to 31 March</td><td>84.6</td><td></td><td>105.49</td><td>(20.89)</td></tr>
<tr><td></td><td></td><td>106.43</td><td></td><td></td></tr>
<tr><td>3 months to 30 June</td><td>116.4</td><td></td><td>106.09</td><td>10.31</td></tr>
<tr><td></td><td></td><td>105.75</td><td></td><td></td></tr>
<tr><td>3 months to 30 September</td><td>93.4</td><td></td><td>106.55</td><td>(13.15)</td></tr>
<tr><td></td><td></td><td>107.35</td><td></td><td></td></tr>
<tr><td>3 months to 31 December</td><td>128.6</td><td></td><td>107.75</td><td>20.85</td></tr>
<tr><td>19X2</td><td></td><td>108.15</td><td></td><td></td></tr>
<tr><td>3 months to 31 March</td><td>91.0</td><td></td><td>108.75</td><td>(17.75)</td></tr>
<tr><td></td><td></td><td>109.35</td><td></td><td></td></tr>
<tr><td>3 months to 30 June</td><td>119.6</td><td></td><td>110.025</td><td>9.575</td></tr>
<tr><td></td><td></td><td>110.70</td><td></td><td></td></tr>
<tr><td>3 months to 30 September</td><td>98.2</td><td></td><td></td><td></td></tr>
<tr><td></td><td></td><td></td><td></td><td></td></tr>
<tr><td>3 months to 31 December</td><td>134.0</td><td></td><td></td><td></td></tr>
</table>

Negative figures are shown in brackets.

Task 5

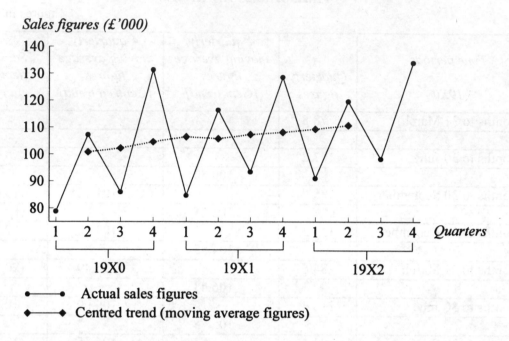

Time series chart – Sales revenues

Period of analysis – Financial years 19X0 – 19X2

An average seasonal effect for a quarter ending on 30 September could be computed as follows:

$$[(15.625) + (13.15)] \div 2 = (28.775) \div 2 = £14,388 \text{ negative seasonal effect (to the nearest £)}$$
$$(19X0) (19X1)$$

Task 6

The multiple bar charts might be presented as follows:

Sales revenues – Quarterly results

Period of analysis – Financial years 19X0 – 19X2

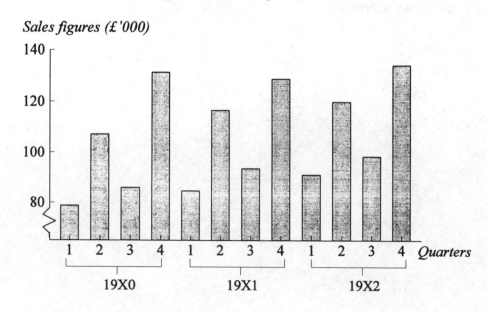

Task 7

A suitable pie chart might be presented as follows:

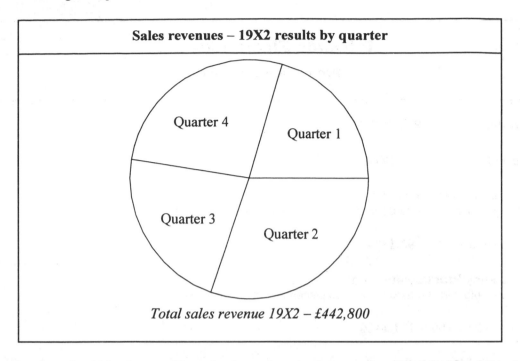

Sales revenues – 19X2 results by quarter

Quarter 4

Quarter 1

Quarter 3

Quarter 2

Total sales revenue 19X2 – £442,800

Tutorial note the chart should be drawn with angles for each sector (measured at the centre of the chart) being:

–   For quarter 1: $(91.0 \div 442.8) \times 360 = 74°$
–   For quarter 2: $(119.6 \div 442.8) \times 360 = 97°$
–   For quarter 3: $(98.2 \div 442.8) \times 360 = 80°$
–   For quarter 4: $(134.0 \div 442.8) \times 360 = 109°$ (All to the nearest degree of angle.)

Task 8

Analysis is as follows (using the company pro forma analysis sheets):

Edwards Electronics Ltd
Production evaluation

Product: TRISTAR TV

Period: 19X2 (Year)

Production-Volume ratio:
(Actual output in standard hours as a percentage of budgeted hours)

$410 \div 440 \times 100 = \mathbf{93.18\%}$

Efficiency/Productivity ratio:
(Actual output in standard hours as a percentage of actual hours)

$410 \div 369 \times 100 = \mathbf{111.11\%}$

Capacity/Usage ratio:
(Actual hours as a percentage of budgeted hours)

$369 \div 440 \times 100 = \mathbf{83.86\%}$

Backing figures

	Units
Standard hour:	
(Budgeted production over budgeted time)	0.5

Actual output in standard hours:

$$\frac{205 \text{ units}}{0.5} = \textbf{410 standard hours}$$

Actual hours worked:

369 hours (given)

Budgeted hours:

440 hours (given)

Tutorial note: the standard hour for the product is 0.5 units. This is the expected/budgeted output in one hour at normal efficiency.

Edwards Electronics Ltd

Production evaluation

Product: TRISTAR TV

Period: 19X2 (Year)

Budgeted sales revenue: £52,800

Budgeted cost of sales: £35,200
(£160 × 220)

Budgeted gross profit margin: £17,600
(This gives budgeted margin of £17,600 ÷ 220 = £80/unit)

Variances

Sales price variance: £950 (F)
[Actual unit sales × (actual SP – budget SP)]

(£240 budgeted selling price vs £245 actual, on 190 units)

Sales volume variance: £2,400 (A)
[Budgeted margin per unit × (actual unit sales – budgeted unit sales)]

(–30 × £80 margin/unit)

Task 9

The completed return for the Association of Electrical Contractors is as follows:

A E C Association of Electrical Contractors
18, Grafton Way, Herts, HA3 4PF

Annual performance results

ROCE [% on owner's investment]	10.44	Debtor period	72.6
Gross margin on sales	45.28	Creditor period	91.3
Net margin on sales [using net profit before tax]	6.62		
Asset turnover [Sales/Net total assets]	1.58	Stock period	129.4

[All periods in days]

Above figures taken from financial statements for the year to/as at 31 December 19X2

Results will be confidentially held and used only to produce general descriptive statistical information for the use of the Association and its members.

UNIT 7

PRACTICE DEVOLVED ASSESSMENT 2

ANSWERS

MILLS CARPETS LTD

Task 1

Possible answers (three required):

– Number or index of houses completed each year – demand for carpets partly depends on this.

– Variations in price of wool – this is the main raw material.

– Sales of carpets by UK manufacturers – shows trends in industry as a whole.

– Volume and price of wool produced by various countries – helps in selection of most plentiful and cheapest sources.

Task 2

	19X1	*19X2*	*19X3*	*19X4*	*19X5*
Total sales value (£'000)	497.07	580.06	657.10	775.59	872.85
Value at 19X1 prices (£'000)	497.07	552.57	594.94	677.80	740.27

Task 3

	19X1	*19X2*	*19X3*	*19X4*	*19X5*
Axminster	100	105	112	116	119
Wilton	100	107	112	121	127
IRP (19X1 = 100)	100	105.0	110.4	114.4	117.9

Task 4

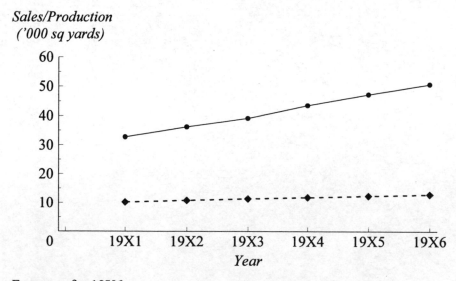

Forecasts for 19X6
Axminster production: 12.8 (ie, 12,800 sq yds)
Wilton production: 50.6 (ie, 50,600 sq yds)

Task 5

Mills Carpets Ltd

To: The sales director

From: Date:

Subject: Sales and price movements and projections: 19X1 to 19X6

Introduction

This report analyses sales and price variations and trends over the period 19X1 to 19X5 and gives a statistical forecast of sales volume for 19X6.

Summary

There has been a steady increase over the five year period in both sales volume and sales value. The latter is an increase in real terms, allowance having been made for inflation.

Sales prices are, however, rising faster than inflation, which is a trend that needs to be halted.

Findings

1   *Sales volume*

There has been a steady increase in sales for both types of carpet over the five-year period, as summarised in the following table:

Production 19X1 to 19X5

Carpet type	*Actual increase ('000 sq yds)*	*% Increase*
Axminster	2.1	20.6
Wilton	14.5	44.3
Combined	16.6	38.7

Production and sales of Wilton carpets has increased at more than twice the rate (44.3%) of Axminster (20.6%).

2   *Prices*

Prices are rising by approximately six index points annually (greater in 19X4 for Wilton). This is greater than the rate of inflation, except for Axminster in 19X2. The overall increases are given below:

Price index for 19X5 (19X1 = 100)

Carpet type	*Index for 19X5*
Axminster	119
Wilton	127
Index of retail prices (19X1 = 100)	118

From this table, it will be seen that the price of Axminster has risen by one point more and Wilton by nine points more than the IRP over the five-year period.

3   *Sales value*

The sales value is increasing both in actual and real terms, as shown by the following table:

Total sales value – 19X1 to 19X5

	Actual increase (£'000)	*% Increase*
Total sales	375.78	75.6
Deflated sales at 19X1 prices	243.20	48.9

Thus there has been an increase in real terms of 48.9% over the five-year period.

4   *Forecasts for 19X6*

Statistical forecasts of sales volume for 19X6 are:

Axminster	12,800 sq yds
Wilton	50,600 sq yds

As the graphs of production are fairly close to straight lines, the extrapolation to 19X6 should be reliable, provided no new factors occur to change the trends.

Conclusions

The following conclusions can be drawn from this analysis:

–   Demand is steadily increasing and, provided no new factors occur, sales volume for the next year should be budgeted at 12,800 square yards of Axminster and 50,600 square yards of Wilton.

–   Up to the present, the value of sales has been steadily increasing in real terms. However, prices are increasing above the rate of inflation and this will result in increasing sales resistance if the trend is allowed to continue. The causes of this rise in prices should be investigated and the trend halted if the company is to remain competitive.

Task 6

	19X2	19X3	19X4
Percentage to turnover:			
Gross profit	51.9	48.9	45.0
Net profit	2.9	2.2	(2.0)
Materials	20.2	17.8	20.0
Labour	15.4	17.8	20.0
Overhead	12.5	15.6	15.0
Administration	25.0	25.6	24.0
Distribution	24.0	21.1	23.0
Percentage change in sales over previous year		(13.5)	11.1
ROCE $\dfrac{\text{Profit before tax}}{\text{Total assets less current liabilities at year end}} \times 100$	5.9%	4.1%	(4.3)%
$\dfrac{\text{Turnover}}{\text{Fixed assets}}$	2.7	2.4	2.9
Current ratio	1.4	1.4	1.4
Quick ratio	0.5	0.5	0.5
Stock turnover $\dfrac{\text{Cost of sales}}{\text{Year-end stock}}$	1.9	1.8	2.1
Raw materials stock turnover $\dfrac{\text{Cost of materials}}{\text{Year-end materials stock}}$	2.1	1.6	2
Debtor collection period	46 days	57 days	55 days

Task 7

To: Board of directors

From: Date:

Subject: Franklin plc – Financial analysis

Profitability

The gross profit percentage is about 50% which has declined to 45% in 19X4. The net profit percentage is, however, very low with a loss made in 19X4.

The decline in gross profitability appears mainly to be due to the increase in labour costs which have increased from 15% to 20% of turnover.

Both administration and distribution costs are greater than 20% of turnover. Further detail would be required on the elements making up these costs.

There has been no growth in sales in the period in money terms. In real terms there has been a decline as the general index of retail prices has increased by 9% from 19X2 to 19X4 $\left(\frac{230 - 211}{211} \times 100 \right)$.

Return on capital employed has fallen from 6% to a negative return. In absolute terms the 6% is anyway not an attractive return.

The poor ROCE figures are reinforced by the low level of turnover to fixed assets (under 3) and stock turnover (about 2).

In brief, this is not a good performance by the company.

Liquidity

The current and quick ratios have remained constant at 1.4 and 0.5 respectively. These need to be compared with our own ratios to determine whether they are too low or too high. On the face of it, however, their constancy implies sound short-term financial management.

In particular, stock levels have not been allowed to grow despite the lack of sales growth and the low stock turnover ratio. Perhaps this indicates that the management have had no plans for growth.

The debtor collection period has extended from 46 to 55 days and this shows some signs of poor credit control management.

Limitations of analysis

(a)   *Cyclical factors*

Many of the ratios are based on successive annual balance sheets at 31 December. The manner in which the assets have been employed in the business at this date may not be representative of the normal level of activity in the business.

Thus stock levels and debtors, for example, may be at a low point at the financial year-end.

(b)   *Lack of detail*

The published accounts contain summary information in many cases. There is insufficient detail on the elements making up an aggregate figure.

(c)   *Accounting policies*

Accounting policies should be consistently applied by the same company but these may be different to ours, making inter-firm comparison difficult.

(d)   *Timeliness of information*

The data is past information from published accounts. The latest information is thus already over a year out of date and may not reflect current circumstances.

UNIT 8

PRACTICE DEVOLVED ASSESSMENT 1

ANSWERS

PREPARING VAT RETURNS

Task 1

VAT RETURN

Value Added Tax Return

For the period

For Official Use

HM Customs and Excise

Registration number   Period

You should be liable to a financial penalty if your completed return and all the VAT payable are not received by the due date.

Due date:

For Official Use

Your VAT Office telehpone number is

REMEMBER

You must include VAT due on EC transactions in boxes 2 & 3 if they occur on or after 1.1.93.

Before you fill in this form please read the notes on the back and the VAT leaflet 'Filling in your VAT return'. Fill in all boxes clearly in ink, and write 'none' where necessary. Don't put a dash or leave any box blank. If there are no pence write "00" in the pence column. Do not enter more than one amount in any box.

For official use	Description	Box		Amount	
	VAT due in this period on sales and other outputs	1	(W1)	£5,985	74
	VAT due in this period on acquisitions from other EC Member States	2		None	
	Total VAT due (the sume of boxes 1 and 2)	3		£5,985	74
	VAT reclaimed in this period on purchases and other inputs (including acquisitions from the EC)	4	(W2)	£4,485	16
	(Difference between boxes 3 and 4)	5	(W3)	£1,500	58
	Total value of sales and all other outputs excluding any VAT, include your box 8 figure	6	(Note 3)	£18,775	00
	Total value of purchases and all other inputs excluding any VAT, include your box 9 figure	7	(Note 5)	£9,811	00
	Total value of all supplies of goods and related services, exlcuding any VAT, to other EC Member States	8		None	00
	Total value of all acquisitions of goods and related services, excluding any VAT, from other EC Member States	9		None	00

Retail schemes.   If you have used any of the schemes in the period covered by this return, enter the relevant letter(s) in this box.

If you are enclosing a payment please tick this box.

DECLARATION: You, or someone on your behalf, must sign below.

I __ ___ ___ ___ ___ ___ ___ ___ ___ ___ declare that the
             (Full name of signatory in BLOCK LETTERS)
information given above is true and complete.

Signature __ ___ ___ ___ ___ ___ ___ Date __ ____ ___ 19 __ __ _

A false declaration can result in prosecution.

CD 2859/N3(04/92)   F3790 (January 1983)

VAT 100

WORKINGS

(1)   3,285.74 (Note 3) + 2,700.00 = £5,985.74

(2)   1,693.61 (Note 5) + 2,500.00 + 291.55 = £4,485.16

(3)   5,985.74 – 4,485.16 = £1,500.58

NOTES

(1)   The basic tax point for goods is the date on which they were collected, delivered or made available to the customer. However if a payment is received before the basic tax point then the date of payment is the date that the supply is treated as taking place.

(2)   If a tax invoice is issued within fourteen days after the basic tax point then the invoice date is treated as the time when the supply took place. Therefore as the invoice to Mr Singh was issued within fourteen days of the date of completion of the work (28 October) then the invoice date of 2 November is the date of supply. The VAT on this invoice will therefore be dealt with in the following VAT accounting period.

(3)   Output VAT

	Net £	*VAT* £
Mr Wilson	80.00	14.00
Mrs Jepson	6,580.00	1,151.50
Mr Wilson	2,820.00	493.50
Ms Clancy	9,295.62	1,626.74
	18,775.62	3,285.74

(4)   If samples are given to a VAT registered trader then they will not be treated as a supply unless two or more identical samples are given to the same person. In such circumstances all but one of the samples is treated as a supply and VAT on them must therefore be accounted for. In this example nine of the samples are therefore treated as a supply with input tax implications. Note the special 'Tax Certificate' format required by Customs to confer entitlement to recover input tax.

(5)   Input VAT

	Net £	*VAT* £
Magnum Kitchens	4,900.00	857.50
Ellse Electricals	827.00	141.83
Ellse Electricals	67.32	11.78
Nicholas Baines	3,900.00	682.50
Deductible input tax	9,694.32	1,693.61
Broken Heart (non-deductible expense)	117.00	20.48
	9,811.32	1,714.09

(6)   Only the debt of £1,957.55 (including VAT) from Mrs P Taylor-Young qualifies for bad debt relief for VAT as in order to qualify for the relief at least six months must have elapsed from the date of supply. Therefore the VAT on this debt £291.55 (£1,957.55 × 7/47) is included in the output tax shown in Box 4 of the VAT return.

VAT account

	£		£
Input VAT		Output VAT	
VAT on purchases	1,693.61	VAT on sales	3,285.74
Understatement of input		Understatement of output	
tax from previous returns	2,500.00	tax from previous returns	2,700.00
Bad debt relief	291.55		
Payable to Customs			
& Excise	1,500.58		
	5,985.74		5,985.74

Task 2

MEMORANDUM

TO: Jean Simons

FROM: The bookkeeper

DATE: 2 November 19X7

SUBJECT: Customs and Excise control visits

Control visits

As VAT is a self-assessed tax it is understandable that Customs and Excise would wish to carry out spot checks to ensure that businesses are accounting correctly for VAT. These spot checks are known as control visits.

The purpose of the visit for the Customs and Excise officer is to ensure that VAT returns have been correctly filled out by reference to the original VAT records. These visits are also designed as a deterrent to fraud.

Such visits are also an ideal opportunity for you to sort out any difficulties that you feel have occurred in practice.

Assessments

If the officer feels that VAT returns have been incorrectly made then he can issue an assessment, in his best judgement, of the additional amount to be paid or repaid. Such an assessment must be made within two years of the end of the accounting period to which it relates or within one year of the necessary evidence becoming available to the officer. This is all subject to an overriding time limit of six years or twenty years if fraud or dishonest conduct is involved.

Task 3

MEMORANDUM

TO: Jean Simons

FROM: The Bookkeeper

DATE: 8 November 19X7

SUBJECT: Your queries

1   There are two types of supply of goods and services for VAT purposes. These are exempt supplies and taxable supplies. Exempt supplies are not subject to VAT. Taxable supplies may be standard rated, taxed at the standard rate of 17.5%, or zero rated, taxed at a rate of 0%.

    In your type of business then it is possible that you might make zero rated supplies. If you were to fit and supply a kitchen in the course of construction of a new property then both your services and the materials and goods used would be zero rated. This does not apply, however, to most kitchen appliances such as fridges and cookers which remain standard rated.

2   If you were to make zero rated supplies then this would not effect the input VAT that you could reclaim from Customs & Excise. All deductible input tax could still be reclaimed.

    However if you were to make exempt supplies as well as standard and/or zero rated supplies then you would be known as a partially exempt trader. For such a trader the VAT on inputs can only be recovered to the extent that they are deemed to relate to the taxable supplies that you make. The VAT on inputs that relate to exempt supplies made is not recoverable.

3   If the owner of a business permanently withdraws goods from the business for private use then this is treated as a supply of goods. Therefore output VAT must be accounted for although based upon cost to the business rather than selling price.

4   For goods on sale or return then the tax point is the earlier of when the goods are adopted by the customer or twelve months after the basic tax point.

    Therefore if you take goods on sale or return you will account for the input VAT either on the date that you decide to take the goods permanently or twelve months after they are delivered to you, whichever is earlier.

5   If a credit note is to be valid documentation for VAT purposes then it must refer to the original invoice for the goods by number and date and the reason for the credit note being issued must be stated.

6   If the total value of the goods purchased, including VAT, is less than £100 then an invoice which shows only the VAT inclusive figure will be valid provided that the invoice also includes the supplier's name, address, VAT registration number, the date of supply, description of the goods and the rate of VAT applicable.

However if the VAT inclusive amount is greater than £100 then this will not be a valid invoice with which to support a claim for input VAT and a full VAT invoice must be requested.

7   Provided that you sell the business whilst you are still a registered trader for VAT purposes then this is not treated as a supply of goods or services. It is simply a change in the taxable person carrying on the business. The new owner can indeed apply to retain your VAT registration number but if he does so he will also inherit the liability for any VAT that may not have been paid.

PRACTICE CENTRAL

ASSESSMENT ACTIVITIES

ANSWERS

TASK 1

BTC (June 1994)

Multiple Bar Chart - Transport Operation

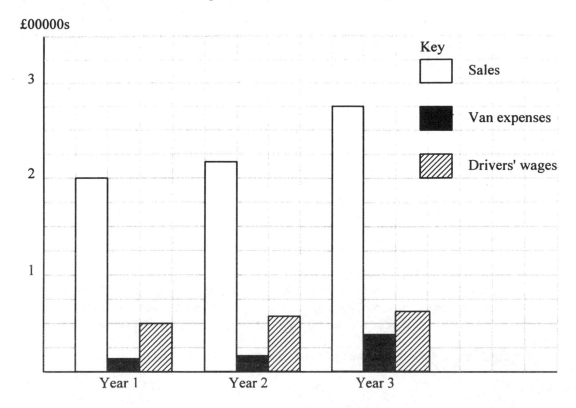

TASK 2

APPENDIX 2			
Years	1	2	3
Sales £s	200,000	202,000	199,000
Van expenses £s	14,000	14,423	16,981
As % of sales	7	7.1	8.5
Drivers' wages £s	52,000	56,600	68,150
As % of sales	26	28.0	34.2
No. of vans	3	3	4
Sales per van £s	66,667	67,333	49,750
No. of deliveries	1,000	1,100	1,400
Sales per delivery £s	200	183.6	142.1

TASK 3

REPORT

TO: General Manager

FROM: Assistant Accountant

DATE: June 1994

REF:

SUBJECT: Transport operation

Section 1

1.1   In Appendix 1, attached to this report, are details of sales and main cost items relating to the above operation. 'Key ratios' have been calculated to assist in interpreting the performance.

1.2   Most of the 'key ratios' have improved; sales have increased, and van expenses are down from 7% to 6.6%, drivers' wages have similarly reduced from 26% to 25% and the number of deliveries has increased. The only hiccup is in the sales per van for Year 3. However, as the new van was purchased during the year a full year's use was not achieved.

1.3   On the basis of Appendix 1 the operation is working efficiently.

Section 2

2.1   In Appendix 2, also attached to this report, the same 'key ratios' were calculated and a different picture emerged. The reason for the difference from Appendix 1 is that inflation has been removed from the figures.

2.2   Sales have hardly changed during the three years. Van expenses and drivers' wages have both increased as a percentage of sales. Sales per van have fallen, indicating that the utilisation of vans is not as good as it used to be. The new 'key ratio' of sales per delivery is interesting as it indicates that smaller deliveries are being made than previously.

2.3   On the basis of Appendix 2 the operation is not working as efficiently as in Year 1.

Section 3

3.1   The transport operation is not as efficient now as it used to be. There is a need to control van expenses and drivers' wages carefully. The fall in sales per delivery could mean that customers are ordering less (although sales have remained steady) or that we are not as efficient in planning our deliveries as we were. Did we need to buy the new van? Static sales could mean a lack of future potential in this sector.

3.2   I believe that, in the future, information of this nature should be produced regularly, at least monthly. Appendix 2 is the model that we should follow as it indicates the underlying quantity changes. One extra 'key ratio' that should be studied is miles per gallon achieved by the vans. This would indicate whether the vans were being efficiently maintained and driven and would also provide a deterrent to anyone attempting to steal petrol.

3.3   This report indicates areas that need investigation.

WMSC (December 1994)

TASK 1

			Workings
In the TT column	- hire charges	16%	1,322 ÷ 8,263
In the total column	- gross profit	47%	3,905 ÷ 8,263
	- net profit	14%	1,185 ÷ 8,263
	- ROCE	35%	1,185 ÷ 3,385
	- utilisation	81%	8,263 ÷ 10,200

TASK 2

TO:	General Manager
FROM:	Assistant Accountant
DATE:	6.12.94
SUBJECT:	**Annual Operating Statement**

Company report

1   The company has had a successful year. The ROCE was better than the industry average because the gross profit to hire charges percentage was better and a fairly high utilisation of capacity was achieved. The net profit to hire charges was below the industry average which may indicate that the general expenses need to be examined.

Ship reports

2   BB provides more than half of the total hire charges and is thus very important to the company. It makes a good return on capital employed, has the lowest general expenses as a percentage of hire charges and has achieved a good level of utilisation.

3   The level of utilisation of SS is disappointing and this is probably the main reason for the general expenses being high and why the ROCE is poor. The gross profit percentage is good but more volume is needed.

4   TT, although only providing a small part of the hire charges for the company, has achieved extremely good results. It has the highest gross and net profit percentages and a very good ROCE. Its utilisation exceeded expectations. If it is possible to increase activity in this area, it should be done.

Proposed investment

5   The proposal to buy a second SS is not supported by the operating statement. Its utilisation was poor and the ROCE the lowest of the three ships. Is this the area where the company should be investing more money?

6   The strength of the competition needs to be assessed before making a decision on where to invest. (Growth of market, availability of labour, innovation in the design of ships, safety etc, all acceptable.)

TASK 3

(a)

			November	
KEY		*Letter*	*% 1994*	*% 1993*
Wages and salaries		A	30	25
Building occupation costs		B	20	25
Agents' commission		E	25	20
General admin. expenses		D	10	15
Depreciation		C	15	15
			100	100

(b)

TO: Admin. Manager

FROM: Assistant Accountant

DATE: 6.12.94

SUBJECT: **November pie charts**

---

1   It is important to stress that in this comparison it is the relative size of the expenses that we are comparing.

2   Segments A and B amount to 50% of the total expenditure for each year but the proportion has changed by A increasing and B reducing.

3   The proportion of E has increased in November 1994 and D has reduced.

4   C is the same proportion in both years.

5   The agents' commission may have increased because the volume of sales increased (a variable expense). The general admin. expenses may have reduced due to more work being tackled in-house rather than by a bureau, eg, computing. (This is backed-up by an increase in wages and salaries in 1994).

(Other reasons could be stated in answer to 5 above.)

CLASS ACTIVITIES

AND ASSESSMENTS

QUESTIONS

UNIT 7

CLASS ACTIVITIES

AND ASSESSMENTS

QUESTIONS

1 BASIC MATHEMATICAL TECHNIQUES

___

1   Activity

Task

Solve the following equations, where possible:

(a) $3x - 2 \quad = \quad 4x - 4$

(b) $4 - 5x \quad = \quad 14 + 12x$

(c) $\dfrac{12 - 3x}{4x + 5} \quad = \quad 4$

(d) $12x + 2y \quad = \quad 4$ and

       $x - 2y \quad = \quad 9$

(e) $10x + 5y \quad = \quad 3 - 2x$ and

       $4x + 10y \quad = \quad 8 - 3x$

(f) $(2x + 5)(x + 1) = \quad 5$

(g) $6x^2 + 12x \quad = \quad 4(5x + 2)$

(h) $3x^2 - 2x + 7 \quad = \quad 0$

(i) $2x^2 - 5x + 4xy = \quad 60$ and

       $3x - y \quad = \quad 9$

2   Activity

Task

A company buys a product from the manufacturer for £900. They feel that they need to make a profit of 35% on the selling price to cover overheads. At what price should the company sell the product?

2 TABULATION OF DATA

1   Activity

During a 10-day sales campaign the numbers of new customers introduced by the 49 members of a company's sales force were as follows:

51	51	52	52	53	53	53
54	55	61	61	61	62	62
62	63	63	63	64	65	66
71	71	71	72	73	73	73
73	74	74	74	74	75	76
77	81	81	81	82	82	83
83	84	85	91	92	92	93

Note: The numbers have been arranged in ascending order.

Tasks

(a)   Calculate the arithmetic mean directly from the above data. (**Note:** You need not write out the data into your answer book).

(b)   Identify and state the median item.

(c)   Summarise the data into a grouped frequency distribution of equal classes starting with 51–60.

(d)   Calculate the arithmetic mean from your grouped frequency distribution.

(e)   Calculate the value of the median from your grouped frequency distribution.

(f)   Explain why the values of the arithmetic mean and median you have calculated from the grouped frequency distribution differ from those you have derived directly from the data.

2   Activity

The Midwich General Hospital operates its own laundry for washing bed-linen, uniforms, doctors' coats, etc. In 19X2, the expenditure on wages relating to the personnel section was £52,188 for administration, £28,340 for supervisors and £111,786 for laundry staff; the expenditure relating to operating expenses was £17,188 on soap powder, £6,485 on water softeners and £3,335 on starch. The expenditure on buildings in 19X2 amounted to £16,427 on maintenance, £31,990 on fuel and £47,468 on equipment and furniture. Similar expenditure in 19X7 was £27,010 on maintenance, £38,460 on fuel and £22,875 on equipment and furniture. Personnel expenditure in 19X7 was £61,342 on administration wages, £24,050 on supervisors' wages and £125,670 on laundry staff wages. Operating expenses were £19,676 on soap powder, £10,004 on water softeners and £4,460 on starch.

Tasks

(a)   The hospital's financial director requires that this data be collated in a good presentational form for the next meeting of the expenditure committee. Represent this data in a single, clearly labelled table.

(b)   Create a second, similar table to show percentage expenditures for each year, and comment upon the trends indicated.

(c)   In 1982, the hospital bed occupancy rate averaged to 82%; in 19X7 this rate was 93%.

Calculate, for both 19X2 and 19X7, the average laundry cost per occupied bed attributable to personnel, to operating expenses and to buildings, if in 19X2 there were 240 beds but in 19X7 220.

Comment on your results.

3   Activity

The table printed below shows the values of UK exports to Japan for the year 19X8, highlighting the ten products whose sales were £40m or more (referred to in the table as 'the top ten'). Also shown are the percentage changes from the previous year.

UK EXPORTS TO JAPAN		
The top ten in 19X8		
	Value (£m)	*% change over 19X7*
Organic chemicals	91	+16
Paintings, drawings, etc	88	−29
Whisky	88	+30
Platinum	72	+255
Electrical controlling and measuring instruments	72	+69
Woollen fabrics	68	+32
Cars	65	+60
Medicaments	56	−14
Jet and gas engines and parts	42	−8
Office and automatic data processing equipment	40	−5
	682	
Other products	1,061	
Total UK exports	1,743	+17

Source: Overseas Trade: October 19X9 (Department of Trade and Industry)

Tasks

(a)   Calculate, to the nearest £m, the export sales of each category and the total for the year 19X7.

(b)   Draw up a table showing the 19X8 and 19X7 figures in adjacent columns.

4   Activity

According to the records of the Department of Trade and Industry reported in the May 19X6 issue of *Monthly Digest of Statistics*, the United Kingdom's exports at 'free on board' values during 19X5 totalled 78,331.4 million pounds, their destinations being: European Community 36,207.3 million pounds, the rest of Europe 9,413.2 million pounds, North America 13,309.9 million pounds, other developed countries 3,791.8 million pounds, oil exporting countries 5,956.9 million pounds, other developing countries 7,923.5 million pounds, centrally planned economies 1,586.9 million pounds and uncategorised exports of low value 141.9 million pounds.

Task

Prepare a table showing the foregoing information rounded in each case to the nearest million pounds, and the percentage relationship of exports of each destination category to the total.

3 DIAGRAMMATIC PRESENTATION

1 Activity

Construct a histogram from the following data which refers to the weights (in kgs) of 42 crates of frozen fish landed at Grimsby:

Class interval	Range of class	Frequency	Height of bar
Weights (kgs)		Number of crates	
10 and less than 15	5	2	2
15 and less than 20	5	5	5
20 and less than 30	10	12	12/2 = 6
30 and less than 40	10	16	16/2 = 8
40 and less than 45	5	7	7

2 Activity

Construct a histogram for the following data relevant to a certain examination, which offered a maximum of 100 marks:

12 candidates obtained fewer than 10 marks
25 obtained 10 to under 25 marks
51 obtained 25 to under 40 marks
48 obtained 40 to under 50 marks
46 obtained 50 to under 60 marks
54 obtained 60 to under 80 marks
and only 8 obtained 80 marks or more

4 GRAPHICAL PRESENTATION

1 Activity

The number of spodgets sold by the 60 sales representatives of Bigtown Novelties plc during April 19X6 were as follows:

55	42	26	59	35	67
32	36	46	34	50	71
56	69	52	51	68	44
40	57	72	60	45	37
52	38	51	62	74	41
66	47	50	61	64	45
51	44	53	41	55	46
38	47	63	58	57	56
53	49	47	43	49	54
43	52	52	48	54	48

Tasks

(a)   Prepare a working paper (*tally sheet*) classifying the sales into categories of five commencing with '25 to 29'.

(b)   Draw the histogram of the distribution.

2 Activity

Sales of Kwikgro, a horticultural chemical, for the six years 19X0 to 19X5 have been as set out below, the average price per ton being quoted alongside:

Year	Sales value £	Average price per ton £
19X0	576,000	80
19X1	671,328	84
19X2	762,552	89
19X3	848,160	95
19X4	988,992	101
19X5	1,076,112	106

Tasks

(a)   Draw a graph showing the tons sold (rounded to nearest 100) for each of the six years.

(b)   Calculate index numbers (with 19X0 = 100) for:

(i)   sales value;
(ii)   average price per ton; and
(iii)   sales volume (tons sold).

3   Activity

During his review of the year's trading to 31 October 19X0, the chairman of Superexports plc said: 'Our sales to countries within the European Community amounted to £786,675 and to the rest of Europe £218,825, whilst sales to North America amounted to £285,400, to other developed countries £92,200 and to developing countries £188,750. Our exports to the oil exporting countries amounted to £145,150 and to countries with centrally planned economies £33,750.'

Tasks

(a)   Prepare a table setting out the company's sales to the different markets, rounding figures to the nearest thousand pounds.

(b)   Using the figures from your table, present the data in the form of a pie chart.

4   Activity

The numbers of visitors to the Borough of Zedtown's local history museum during the years 19X6 and 19X7 were as follows:

	19X6	*19X7*
January	250	300
February	450	500
March	500	500
April	650	700
May	800	800
June	850	900
July	900	1,000
August	1,000	1,100
September	750	1,000
October	600	700
November	350	500
December	200	350

Task

Present the foregoing data as a Z chart.

5 TIME SERIES ANALYSIS

1 Activity

The following is a time series of an organisation's quarterly profits:

Time series: Quarterly profits of an organisation

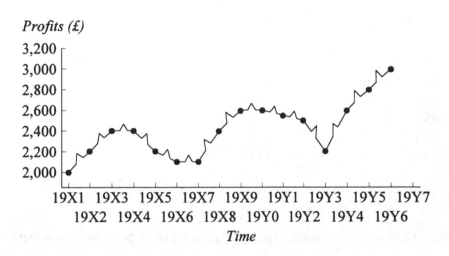

Profits (£)

Task

Using the above graph as a basis, explain and comment on the limitations of the:

(a)   long-term trend;
(b)   cyclical movement; and
(c)   seasonal variations.

2 Activity

The sales of golf equipment by a large department store are shown for each period of three months as follows:

	19X8 £'000	19X9 £'000	19Y0 £'000	19Y1 £'000
First quarter		8	20	40
Second quarter		30	50	62
Third quarter		60	80	92
Fourth quarter	24	20	40	

Tasks

(a)   Using an additive model, find the centred moving average trend.
(b)   Find the average seasonal variation for each quarter.
(c)   Predict sales for the last quarter of 19Y1 and the first quarter of 19Y2, stating any assumption

6 INDEX NUMBERS

1 Activity

A pension commences in 19X1 at £10,000 per year.

Task

Calculate the indexed pension for 19X2 to 19X5, given the following values of the IRP:

Year	IRP
19X1	102.7
19X2	107.0
19X3	116.0
19X4	126.9
19X5	134.3

2 Activity

The sales of Confinco Ltd for five years and the corresponding retail price index numbers were:

Year	Sales £m	Index of retail prices
19X1	50.0	102.7
19X2	51.2	107.0
19X3	52.8	116.0
19X4	55.8	126.9
19X5	56.4	134.3

Task

You are required to produce a series of sales values relative to 19X2, deflated to take account of inflation.

3 Activity

The data below refer to average earnings index numbers in Great Britain for different sectors of industry, 19X8 = 100, and the retail price index, 19X7 = 100.

Date	Whole economy	Production industries	Service industries	Retail price index
19X8	100	100	100	107
Feb 19X9	104.6	104.9	104.4	111.5
May 19X9	107.5	108.1	107.2	115.0
Aug 19X9	109.1	109.2	108.7	115.8
Nov 19X9	112.8	112.9	112.7	118.5

Feb 19Y0	114.0	114.3	113.7	120.2
May 19Y0	118.5	118.2	118.6	126.2
Aug 19Y0	120.9	119.7	121.1	128.1
Nov 19Y0	123.8	123.7	123.0	130.0
Feb 19Y1	124.7	125.2	123.8	130.9
May 19Y1	128.1	129.2	127.1	133.5
Aug 19Y1	130.8	130.2	130.4	134.1
Nov 19Y1	130.8	131.8	129.7	135.6

(Source: Employment Gazette, January 19Y2)

Tasks

(a)   Using 19X8 = 100 as base throughout, deflate the production industries index and comment briefly on the *real* (inflation adjusted) change in its average earnings over the period 19X9–19Y1.

(b)   A retired person from the service industries had an index-linked pension of £5,000 a year, starting in May 19X9 and updated each November in line with the average earnings index for that sector. Find the pension rates for November in each of the years 19X9, 19Y0, 19Y1 and comment on their value in *real* terms.

4   Activity

(a)   The following data have been taken from the general index of retail prices table published in the Monthly Digest of Statistics and relate to September 19X9:

	Group	Weight	Index
1	Food	154	111.3
2	Catering	49	118.0
3	Alcoholic drink	83	114.7
4	Tobacco	36	106.4
5	Housing	175	138.2
6	Fuel and light	54	109.0
7	Household goods	71	110.9
8	Household services	41	113.2
9	Clothing and footwear	73	111.0
10	Personal goods and services	37	115.6
11	Motoring expenditure	128	115.1
12	Fares and other travel costs	23	116.3
13	Leisure goods	47	107.8
14	Leisure services	29	117.2

Tasks

(i)   Calculate the 'All groups' index number for September 19X9.

(ii)   Calculate an index number to represent expenditure on motoring and travel ie, groups 11 and 12.

(b)   Included in Group 5 (Housing) is expenditure on mortgage interest payments which has a weighting of 60 and an index number 168.2.

Task

Calculate an index number representing all groups excluding expenditure on mortgage interest.

Note: In your workings you may identify the groups by their reference numbers to save time.

7 MAIN TYPES OF PERFORMANCE INDICATORS

1 Activity

Task

Two examples of comparisons are given below. Give your opinion as to which organisation is better and briefly state why your opinion may be incorrect.

(a)   Two similar authorities provide home help services. The time spent by home help workers on each case per week averages to approximately one hour in one authority and one and a half hours in the other.

(b)   There are two towns of similar size, and each has a public library. The total number of books in one library totals 18,000, in the other there are 30,000.

2 Activity

The following information relates to two hospitals for the year ended 31 December 19X5:

	St Matthew's		St Mark's	
Number of in-patients	15,400		710	
Average stay per in-patient	10 days		156 days	
Total number of out-patient attendances	130,000		3,500	
Number of available beds	510		320	
Average number of beds occupied	402		307	
Cost analysis	*In-patients* £	*Out-patients* £	*In-patients* £	*Out-patients* £
A Patient care services				
1 Direct treatment services and supplies, eg. nursing staff	6,213,900	1,076,400	1,793,204	70,490
2 Medical supporting services				
2.1 Diagnostic, eg, pathology	480,480	312,000	22,152	20,650
2.2 Other services, eg, occupational therapy	237,160	288,600	77,532	27,790
B General services				
1 Patient related, eg, catering	634,480	15,600	399,843	7,700
2 General, eg, administration	2,196,760	947,700	1,412,900	56,700

Note: In-patients are those who receive treatment whilst remaining in hospital. Out-patients visit hospital during the day to receive treatment.

Tasks

(a)   Prepare separate statements for each hospital for each cost heading:

       (i)   cost per in-patient day, £ to two decimal places;
      (ii)   cost per out-patient attendance, £ to two decimal places.

      A blank statement is provided overleaf.

(b)   Calculate for each hospital the bed-occupation percentage.

(c)   Comment briefly on your findings.

COST STATEMENTS FOR THE YEAR ENDED 31 DECEMBER 19X6

	St Matthew's Hospital		St Mark's Hospital	
	Cost per in-patient day	*Cost per out-patient attendance*	*Cost per in-patient day*	*Cost per out-patient attendance*
A Patient services	£	£	£	£
1 Direct treatment service and supplies				
2 Medical supporting services:				
2.1 Diagnostic				
2.2 Other services				
B General services				
1 Patient related				
2 General				
Total	———	———	———	———
	———	———	———	———

8 WRITING REPORTS

1 Activity

Matthewson Taylor are a large media and communications group. They publish novels, academic textbooks, student guides and books about films and music; they publish a number of general interest and specialist interest magazines and journals; they produce and distribute records, pre-recorded tapes and compact discs; and they produce television programmes which are sold to corporations for broadcast in the UK and overseas. Their head offices are located at Third Floor, Matthewson House, 44–48 Fatter Lane, London EC9A 2HW. You work there in the group's central accounts department as accounts supervisor. In all there are 11 people working in the accounts department:

Mr John Davis	Chief accountant
Donna Pountney	Chief accountant's secretary
Balvinder Rai	Financial accountant
YOU	Accounts supervisor
Margaret Korn	Wages supervisor
Justine Taylor) Andrew Hughes)	Wages clerks
Grace Phillips	Credit control clerk
Stuart Parson) Surinder Patel)	Sales ledger clerks
Mary Ho	Junior accounting technician

It is Thursday 3 December 19X7. Immediately after lunch, Balvinder Rai enters your office. Although he is not someone who is easily worried by problems at work, he looks worried as he walks in. He closes your door and asks if he can speak with you in confidence. After he has reminded you that Mary Ho joined the accounts department in August this year and that shortly after she took part in the group's induction programme, he pauses. After a few moments he says what has been troubling him. Reports have been fed back to him quite frankly. Mary is not pulling her weight.

Balvinder explains the nature of the reports he has received about Mary. Harry Smith, the group's head of personnel, has produced a written report about her, expressing his reservations. Although she attended all the sessions in the induction programme, he felt that she was less than enthusiastic about these sessions and often appeared distracted. Matthewson Taylor do not like to unsettle new employees by requiring them to take on all their duties immediately they start working for the group. Rather they prefer to have them work closely with a number of key employees in their department until they are sufficiently settled in to take up all their duties. Mary has been working with Margaret Korn and Grace Phillips.

They are both long-serving employees who have significant experience of assisting your new employees in their first days with the accounts department. They have indicated to Balvinder that they felt Mary was not progressing in her new job.

While they were happy to have her observe them in the performance of their duties in the initial period she was with them, they were not happy with the way in which she did not begin to take on more responsibility. Finally, Mary's apparent lack of understanding of the duties she is expected to perform has caused her to express her frustration the form of emotional outbursts.

All in all this is clearly not a happy situation. Balvinder explains that he has a number of problems here. He says that he feels guilty that news of Mary's unsatisfactory performance had not come to his notice earlier. He thinks that if he were to approach Mary she might feel he was disciplining her and that she could resign on the spot. He would be unhappy to have this happen, given the time, money and energy which the group had already expended on Mary. But he does feel that some form of action needs to be taken to remedy this situation. You pause for a moment and then speak. You feel it would be better if you were to speak with Mary and try to find out the reasons for her lack of enthusiasm. Balvinder readily agrees to your suggestion and asks you if you would do what you propose.

Later on that afternoon you call Mary into your office. You explain, in a diplomatic fashion, the nature of the reports which have been made about her behaviour. Once Mary understands what it is you are talking about she makes a half-hearted attempt to excuse herself but then breaks down in tears. You reassure her and, once she has calmed down, ask her what the matter is. She explains that she has been distracted by a number of long-running problems of a domestic nature at home, that she has been struggling in her work as a result of this, but that she feels the problems at home have now been resolved. By the time you conclude your interview with Mary you are convinced that she is genuine in her stating that her problems are now over and are persuaded by her promising to commit herself to the efficient performance of her duties at work. After Mary has left your office you go to Balvinder's office. You explain what has taken place. He is grateful that matters appear to have been resolved and asks you to do two things for him. Firstly he asks you to produce a written report containing full details of the incident. Secondly, as this matter cannot pass without some formal comment, he asks you to produce the draft of a letter, written on his behalf, to Mary stating that he is pleased that she is now determined to commit herself to her job but that she will have to be closely monitored in the near future to ensure that she does not fall back into her old ways. You go back to your office to produce the report.

Task

Write the detailed report about this incident. You must include background information about Mary's poor performance, an account of the interview you conducted with Mary and an explanation of the action you took.

9 ORGANISATIONS - STRUCTURE AND PERFORMANCE

1   Activity

Explain how organisations are structured. Use an organisation chart to illustrate your answer.

2   Activity

Explain how information from different sources within an organisation can be reconciled and why this is important.

UNIT 8

CLASS ACTIVITIES

AND ASSESSMENTS

QUESTIONS

1 INTRODUCTION TO VAT - SUPPLIES AND REGISTRATION

1 Activity

Laura started trading on 1 July 1995. During her first 18 months of trading her turnover figures were:

	1995 £	1996 £
January		3,700
February		3,900
March		4,200
April		4,200
May		4,300
June		4,400
July	3,000	4,400
August	3,200	4,300
September	3,200	4,400
October	3,500	4,400
November	3,600	4,500
December	3,600	4,600

When is Laura liable to register for VAT?

2 Activity

In the preceding activity Laura started trading on 1 July 1995. During her first 18 months of trading her turnover figures were:

	1995 £	1996 £
January		3,700
February		3,900
March		4,200
April		4,200
May		4,300
June		4,400
July	3,000	4,400
August	3,200	4,300
September	3,200	4,400
October	3,500	4,400
November	3,600	4,500
December	3,600	4,600

Would it make any difference to the date Laura was required to register for VAT (in Activity 1) if in February 1996 she was awarded a contract which would result in additional turnover of £43,250 per month?

3   Activity

Gareth makes furniture, some for offices and some for domestic use. He sells two consignments, each for £2,200 (exclusive of VAT). One customer, Alex, is registered for VAT, whilst the other, Catherine, is not. The raw materials cost £2,350, and the trader incurs overheads of £470 (both of these are VAT inclusive amounts).

Consider the effect of these transactions on Gareth, Alex and Catherine if:

(a)   Gareth is not registered for VAT.
(b)   Gareth is registered for VAT.

2 VAT INVOICES, VAT PERIODS, RECORDS REQUIRED

1 Activity

Supplier Ltd supplies the following goods to Customer Ltd, of the Business Park, Someton, SN2 2RR:

> 5 boxes of card @ £6.50 per box
> 10 printer ribbons @ £2.75 each
> 12 boxes of pencils @ 95p each
> 1 Fax machine @ £455 each
> 10 stacking chairs @ £27.99 each.

The goods were despatched on 28 February 1997.

Prepare the tax invoice, assuming that today's date is 4 March 1997, and that Customer Ltd will receive a 3% discount if the invoice is settled within 14 days. The last invoice was numbered 6797.

2 Activity

Supplier Ltd supplies the following goods to Buyers Ltd, of 2 Church Lane, Someton, SN5 6NT:

> 12 cartons of files @ £5.25 per carton
> 8 cases of plastic cups @ £3.78 per case
> 50 biros @ 25p each
> 1 coffee machine @ £206.99 each
> 200 bars of chocolate @ 19p each.

The goods were despatched on 12 March 1997.

Prepare the tax invoice, assuming that today's date is 15 March 1997, and that Buyers Ltd will receive a 2% discount if the invoice is settled within 14 days. The last invoice was numbered 7013.

3 Activity

Anita Prakash has the following transactions:

	£
Sales on credit (including VAT)	1,175
Purchases on credit (excluding VAT)	600
Cash sales (including VAT)	470
Cash purchases (excluding VAT)	200
Cash receipts from debtors	770
Cash payments to creditors	450

All sales and purchases are standard rated for VAT purposes.

Write up the books of prime entry, assuming sales and purchases day books are kept only for credit sales and purchases, and write up the ledger accounts.

Sales day book

Date	Details	Total £	VAT £	Sales £	Other £

Purchases day book

Date	Details	Total £	VAT £	Purchases £	Wages £	Etc £

Cash receipts book

Date	Details	Disc £	Total £	VAT £	Sales £	Debtors £

Cash payments book

Date	Details	Disc £	Total £	VAT £	Purchases £	Creditors £

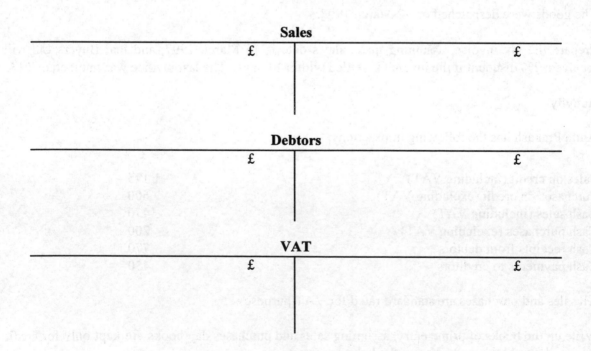

Sales

£	£

Debtors

£	£

VAT

£	£

Purchases

	£		£

Creditors

	£		£

Cash

	£		£

4   Activity

A trader sells goods for £2,000 plus VAT at 17.5%. What is the VAT on these goods and the total price that they will be sold at?

5   Activity

A trader buys goods for £705 including VAT at 17.5%. How much is the VAT included in this price?

6   Activity

Goods are to be sold for £1,000 plus VAT at 17.5%. The terms of the sale are that a 3% cash discount is offered for payment within 10 days and a 2% discount for payment within 21 days.

What amounts would appear on the invoice for the sale of the goods and the VAT?

7   Activity

The total price of some goods was £235 and the VAT included was just £30. Could this be correct and for what reasons?

3 COMPLETING THE VAT RETURN

1   Activity

A trader provides the following information for his VAT quarter ended 30 April 1997.

He has made the following large sales:

Invoice No	Net	Rate of VAT	Rate of cash discount
1	£8,000	standard	2%
2	£7,000	zero	2%
3	£15,000	standard	5%

Invoice number 2 was in respect of goods despatched to France.

He has made various purchases. He has a bundle of less detailed invoices totalling £1,504 in which VAT was included at the rate of 17.5%. In addition he has three invoices from suppliers for £4,700, £2,350 and £5,875 (including VAT).

He also purchased goods from Holland in March, costing £2,000.

He has paid wages of £5,000, and paid bank interest of £1,100.

Show the entries that would appear on the VAT return for the three months to 30 April 1997.

Value Added Tax Return

For the period

For Official Use

HM Customs and Excise

Registration number   Period

You could be liable to a financial penalty if your completed return and all the VAT payable are not received by the due date.

Due date:

For Official Use	

Your VAT Office telehpone number is

ATTENTION

If you are using Retail Scheme B1, D or J, please remember to carry out your annual adjustment at the appropriate time.

Before you fill in this form please read the notes on the back and the VAT leaflet 'Filling in your VAT return'. Fill in all boxes clearly in ink, and write 'none' where necessary. Don't put a dash or leave any box blank. If there are no pence write "00" in the pence column. Do not enter more than one amount in any box.

For official use			
	VAT due in this period on sales and other outputs	1	
	VAT due in this period on acquisitions from other EC Member States	2	
	Total VAT due (the sum of boxes 1 and 2)	3	
	VAT reclaimed in this period on purchases and other inputs (including acquisitions from the EC)	4	
	Net VAT to be paid to Customs or reclaimed by you (Difference between boxes 3 and 4)	5	
	Total value of sales and all other outputs excluding any VAT, include your box 8 figure	6	00
	Total value of purchases and all other inputs excluding any VAT, include your box 9 figure	7	00
	Total value of all supplies of goods and related services, excluding any VAT, to other EC Member States	8	00
	Total value of all acquisitions of goods and related services, excluding any VAT, from other EC Member States	9	00

Retail schemes.   If you have used any of the schemes in the period covered by this return, enter the relevant letter(s) in this box.

If you are enclosing a payment please tick this box.

DECLARATION: You, or someone on your behalf, must sign below.

I _ __ ___ ___ ___ ___ ___ ___ ___ __ declare that the

(Full name of signatory in BLOCK LETTERS)

information given above is true and complete.

Signature _ __ __ __ __ __ __ _Date _ ___ __19 _ __ _

A false declaration can result in prosecution.

CD 2859/N3(08/93)   F3790 (February 1994)

VAT 100

2   Activity

Jane paid VAT as follows:

Return period ended	VAT £	Date paid
30.6.96	11,500	18.11.96
30.9.96	9,200	18.11.96
31.12.96	10,800	29.1.97
31.3.97	8,900	10.5.97

What surcharge penalties will Jane be liable to?

3   Activity

Michael discovered that he had understated his output tax on his VAT return for the 3 months to 30 April 1997 by £76, but that he had also understated his input tax by £139.

If his outputs for the quarter to 31 July were £23,000, excluding VAT of £4,025, and his inputs were £16,000, excluding VAT of £2,800, what entries should he make on his VAT return for the quarter to 31 July 1997?

Value Added Tax Return

For the period

For Official Use

**HM Customs
and Excise**

Registration number

Period

**You could be liable to a financial
penalty if your completed return and all
the VAT payable are not received by the
due date.**

Due date:

| For
Official
Use | |

Your VAT Office telehpone number is

ATTENTION

**If you are using Retail Scheme B1,
D or J, please remember to carry
out your annual adjustment at the
appropriate time.**

Before you fill in this form please read the notes on the back and the VAT leaflet 'Filling in your VAT return'. Fill in
all boxes clearly in ink, and write 'none' where necessary. Don't put a dash or leave any box blank. If there are no
pence write "00" in the pence column. Do not enter more than one amount in any box.

For official use	VAT due in this period on sales and other outputs	1	
	VAT due in this period on acquisitions from other EC Member States	2	
	Total VAT due (the sum of boxes 1 and 2)	3	
	VAT reclaimed in this period on purchases and other inputs (including acquisitions from the EC)	4	
	Net VAT to be paid to Customs or reclaimed by you (Difference between boxes 3 and 4)	5	
	Total value of sales and all other outputs excluding any VAT, include your box 8 figure	6	00
	Total value of purchases and all other inputs excluding any VAT, include your box 9 figure	7	00
	Total value of all supplies of goods and related services, excluding any VAT, to other EC Member States	8	00
	Total value of all acquisitions of goods and related services, excluding any VAT, from other EC Member States	9	00

Retail schemes.   If you have used any of the schemes in the
period covered by this return, enter the relevant letter(s) in this box.

If you are enclosing
a payment please
tick this box.

DECLARATION: You, or someone on your behalf, must sign below.

I __ __ __ __ __ __ __ __ __ __ __ declare that the

(Full name of signatory in BLOCK LETTERS)

information given above is true and complete.

Signature __ __ __ __ __ __ __ Date __ ____ __19 __ __ __

A false declaration can result in prosecution.

CD 2859/N3(08/93)   F3790 (February 1994)

VAT 100

4 SPECIAL CASES

1 Activity

Arnold carries on three activities which give rise to:

(a)   taxable supplies;

(b)   exempt supplies for which input tax is wholly disallowed subject to the *de minimis* limit; and

(c)   supplies which are outside the scope of VAT for which input tax is wholly disallowed.

Relevant figures for the quarter ended 30 June 1997 are:

Activity	Attributable Input tax £
Standard rated supplies (£24,000)	10,500
Zero rated supplies (£8,000)	3,500
Exempt supplies (£9,300)	4,000
	18,000
Overheads	5,000
Total input tax	23,000

Calculate the recoverable input tax for the quarter ended 30 June 1997.

2 Activity

In the year to 30 November 1996 a company has a VAT liability of £2,400,000. Previously the liability had not exceeded £2m. The total VAT liability for the quarter ended 31 August 1997 is £550,000.

How much VAT will be paid to Customs & Excise, and on what dates, for the quarter to 31 August 1997?

5 ADMINISTRATION

1 Activity

Harriet comes to you for some VAT advice. She gives you the following information:

(a)   She started trading on 1 January 1996.

(b)   She runs a small business selling hand made clothes.

(c)   Her monthly turnover is £4,000, of which £2,500 is from the sale of young children's clothes and £1,500 from the sale of adults clothes.

(d)   Her purchases amount to £1,175 per month.

(e)   She asks if she should register for VAT.

(f)   The date is now October 1997.

UNIT 7

PRACTICE DEVOLVED ASSESSMENT 3

QUESTIONS

B BLACK LTD

Time allowed 3 hours

B Black Ltd is a manufacturer of medical appliances. You are Roger Howarth, an accounting technician, who has recently been employed by the company. You report directly to Dave Bannister, the Financial Controller who also has been recently appointed. He requires your assistance in analysing the sales performance of the company in the last three years.

He supplies you with the following data.

Analysis of sales			
	19X2	*19X3*	*19X4*
	£	£	£
United Kingdom	5,436,900	5,001,948	4,651,812
Germany	2,340,988	2,153,709	2,304,469
France	1,400,660	1,778,838	1,761,050
Cyprus	156,444	195,555	244,444
Spain	234,909	281,891	507,403
Rest of Europe	189,000	204,120	208,202
USA	0	34,920	45,396
Canada	34,600	55,360	84,147
Total	9,793,501	9,706,341	9,806,923
UK RPI	383.5	406.5	422.8

Task 1

Dave Bannister wants you to present a summary of the above data for the purposes of presenting a report to the Finance Director. The UK, Germany and France should be separately identified but the rest of Europe should be grouped. The USA and Canada should also be grouped.

He also wants the 19X2 and 19X3 figures uplifted to 19X4 price levels using the RPI shown on his schedule and also the figures to be shown in thousands of pounds.

Prepare a summary schedule as he requests. In addition, show workings so that he understands how you have adjusted the data for price changes.

Task 2

Dave Bannister now wants you to use the sales figures from Task 1 to produce a table of percentage changes. Headings are given below, together with space for the insertion of the figures. Compute the percentages to the nearest unit.

Analysis of sales: Percentage change						
	19X2 to 19X3		*19X3 to 19X4*		*19X2 to 19X4*	
	Nominal	*'Real'*	*Nominal*	*'Real'*	*Nominal*	*'Real'*
United Kingdom						
Germany						
France						
Rest of Europe						
USA and Canada						

Task 3

Dave Bannister has now decided he needs some pictorial representation of the data. He therefore asks you to do two pie charts; one analysing sales in 19X2 and one for 19X4. The groupings should be as for the previous analyses.

Task 4

Dave Bannister is pleased with the work you have done so far. He asks you to prepare some notes which will draw attention to the key points of the summarised data. He wants a brief paragraph to accompany each section of the proposed report ie:

Analysis of sales: Money and real terms
Analysis of sales: Percentage change
Analysis of sales by area: Pie charts

Task 5

Dave Bannister now has a different task for you. The production manager, Jim Swale, has asked for advice on how to construct and use Z charts in order to monitor production of the major items of medical appliances produced. At Dave's request he has supplied a note of production of one of the product lines (artificial hips) for the past two years. The note is shown below.

MEMORANDUM

TO: Dave Bannister

FROM: Jim Swale

DATE: X August 19X5

SUBJECT: **Z Charts**

Production of one of the product lines (artificial hips) for the past two calendar years is shown below. I assume it doesn't make any difference that the period is different to the financial accounting periods. It is more convenient to me to review production on a calendar year basis.

Monthly production ('000 units)

Month	19X3	19X4
Jan	5.3	7.5
Feb	8.0	6.7
Mar	4.7	3.5
Apr	7.8	6.1
May	6.9	5.6
Jun	3.7	3.7
Jul	1.7	2.7
Aug	3.0	4.2
Sep	5.2	6.3
Oct	2.4	3.9
Nov	1.6	3.0
Dec	5.0	6.3
	——	——
	55.3	59.5
	——	——

Thanks for the help.

Dave asks you, using these values as an illustration, to draft a memo to the production manager explaining the construction, use and interpretation of Z charts. The actual Z chart for 19X4 should be constructed as an example, using the grid below or graph paper if you prefer.

UNIT 7

PRACTICE CENTRAL ASSESSMENT 1

QUESTIONS

SHELBECK MANUFACTURING COMPANY

Time allowed 3 hours

BACKGROUND TO CASE STUDY

The Shelbeck Manufacturing Company makes and sells a wide variety of leisure goods including patio furniture, saunas and golf equipment. At the end of the previous financial year the managing director was concerned about the downward trend in monthly sales due to the recession. The company began to offer discounts on a wide range of their goods to generate more sales income. He was delighted when the sales report showed an increase in sales from £16.2 million to £19.0 million. However he was extremely concerned when the final audited accounts showed a drop in profit from £2.6 million to £2.2 million.

The company has invested in new machinery in the division which manufactures golf equipment and is intending to upgrade the patio furniture machinery over the coming two years. He is now concerned that the company will not generate the necessary profit to finance this capital project. The profit and loss accounts and the balance sheets for the last two financial years are shown below.

Profit and loss for year to 31 December

	19X3 £'000	19X2 £'000
Sales	19,000	16,200
Cost of sales	14,400	11,500
Gross profit	4,600	4,700
Distribution costs	(850)	(700)
Administration costs	(950)	(900)
Loan interest	(600)	(500)
	2,200	2,600

Balance sheet at 31 December

	19X3 £'000	19X3 £'000	19X2 £'000	19X2 £'000
Fixed assets		12,000		10,000
Current assets				
Stock	5,400		4,500	
Debtors	4,600	10,000	3,500	8,000
		22,000		18,000
Current liabilities				
Bank overdraft	600		500	
Creditors	5,150	5,750	4,250	4,750
		16,250		13,250
Share capital and reserves		9,950		7,750
Loan		6,300		5,500
		16,250		13,250

Task 1

You have been asked to prepare a report on the effect of the sales promotion.

As a preliminary step you need to analyse the accounts and to calculate the percentage increase or decrease in sales, expenses and gross and net profit. In addition you also need to calculate the following ratios for both years.

(1)   Gross profit percentage.
(2)   Net profit percentage.
(3)   Return on capital employed.
(4)   Current ratio.
(5)   Liquidity ratio.
(6)   Debtor collection period.

Prepare all the above calculations and include them below as an appendix to the report.

APPENDIX TO REPORT

Task 2

Write the report, referred to in task 1, to the managing director explaining the effect the sales volume promotion has had on the results of the company. (Use the figures calculated in Task 1.) The report should also indicate any recommendations on future selling policy.

REPORT

TO:

FROM:

DATE:

SUBJECT:

UNIT 8

PRACTICE DEVOLVED ASSESSMENT 2

QUESTIONS

PREPARING VAT RETURNS

Time allowed 1 hour

This assessment contains 9 tasks. It should be completed in accordance with the working instructions confirmed to you by your course tutor. All work should be in ink and no tippex or equivalent materials should be used.

You will require a copy of the present VAT Guide 700 in order to complete this assessment as you will need to demonstrate practical use of the guide.

Edwards Electronics Ltd is a VAT-registered business. It supplies electronic goods directly to the public and to other trading businesses in the UK and overseas. The tasks which follow are based on the business affairs of the company. You are employed as an Assistant Accountant of the company.

Task 1.

You have received the following note from Wesley Hawkes, a colleague in your office. Respond to Wesley's request. Do so in the form of short, but fully explanative, notes alongside the documents attached to his request, adding if necessary by way of additional comment on the office note paper provided.

OFFICE NOTE

Edwards Electronics Ltd

I'm still having some problems in fully understanding VAT principles & calculation and wondered if you could help.

In particular:

- *If I receive a petty cash voucher that says that the total amount paid is inclusive of VAT at a particular rate, can I split off the VAT we have borne in the petty cash book and treat it as reclaimable input tax?*

- *How do I work out the VAT in such cases where the VAT-inclusive figure is the only one given? (...could you show me examples of the calculations for the past/old receipts I have attached?...Thanks...)*

- *I still haven't fully understood how VAT figures are calculated on sales invoices. For example, the attached invoice includes VAT but the figure doesn't seem to be calculated @ 17.5%. Is it correct? If so, how has it been worked out?...*

Thanks for your help.

Wesley
29th March 1996

Attached petty cash receipts:

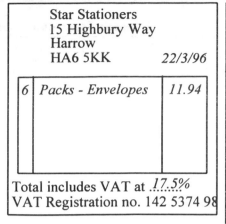

Star Stationers
15 Highbury Way
Harrow
HA6 5KK   *22/3/96*

| 6 | *Packs - Envelopes* | *11.94* |

Total includes VAT at ..*17.5%*
VAT Registration no. 142 5374 98

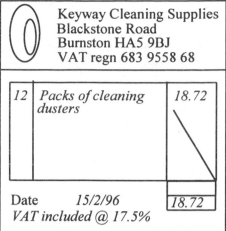

Keyway Cleaning Supplies
Blackstone Road
Burnston HA5 9BJ
VAT regn 683 9558 68

| 12 | *Packs of cleaning dusters* | *18.72* |

Date   *15/2/96* | *18.72* |
VAT included @ 17.5%

Comment

Attached invoice: **Comment:**

Timber Industrie plc
18 Grove Lane
Poole, Dorset   Tel: 0202 420670
BH1S 5BJ   Fax: 0202 420816

Date: 28.2.96   Invoice No. 2390
                     Your ref: JH/9246

No	Items	Item No	£
20	1/CIRCUITS [Unit price £141.07] **Special discount 5%**	IC32	2,680.33

Subtotal   £2,680.33
Edwards Electr's Ltd | VAT   £459.67
22 Broadway Road   Total £3,140.00
Harrow
LONDON   Terms 2%, 30days
HA14 5ON   Net 60days

VAT Reg No 211 3615 92

Notepaper for additional comment:

OFFICE NOTE

Edwards Electronics Ltd

Task 2

Edward Electronics Ltd is required to submit VAT returns for quarters running to the ends of February, May, August & November annually. The returns are about to be prepared for the quarter ending 31st May 1996.

Included in the company records for the quarter to 31st May 1996 are the following invoices and receipts. These have been passed to you for review. You have been asked to confirm whether each is acceptable as a piece of VAT documentation - ie, either as a valid VAT sales invoice or as a valid VAT invoice or receipt for inputs or purchases. The input receipts and invoices will be used to support appropriate offset against VAT on business sales in the company VAT returns provided they are valid.

You are required to check all calculations in addition to other detail.

```
LCP London Car Parks Ltd
        1, Bryan Street
        London   WC1R 5AD

Carpark at. Regents Hill ...............

┌──────────┐
│ £ 8.50p  │  Includes VAT at the
└──────────┘  rate of 17.5%

Date. 26th March 1996 ...............

VAT reg no. 762 8145 85
```

```
            Fastprint Ltd
        14 Elmers End Road
            Beckenham
             BR2 4PD
        VAT No. 238 1457 86

Envelopes          £23.70
Headed Ppr         £18.30
Notepads           £28.00
Business Cards     £56.00
            TL    £126.00

Includes VAT at the
rate of 17.5%

20–04–96
```

```
            Fastprint Ltd
        14 Elmers End Road
            Beckenham
             BR2 4PD
        VAT No. 238 1457 86

Envelopes          £12.20
Notepads           £22.20
            TL     £34.40

Includes VAT at the
rate of 17.5%

20–04–96
```

```
Tumblers

Supply of half-dozen drinking
glasses                  £ 8.60
            VAT        £ 1.51
            TL         £10.11

VAT included @ 17.5%
VAT registration no. 645 8667 95
```

INVOICE

Edwards Electronics
22, Boundary Road
Harrow
London
H14 5ON

Tel: 062 249 0896
Fax: 062 467 8899
VAT Reg No 488 7657 81

Date/Tax Point: 14 April 1996
Order No: PLP 000019
To: 25 Supervision TV sets

£15,500.00

VAT @ 17.5%   £2,712.50

Invoice Value   £18,212.50

James Video Store
14 Hamleton Road
Harrow, MIDDLX,
HA14 5PL

Terms 2%/30days
Net 60days

(SE) **Southern Electric**

Registered address:
15 Wimpole Street
London
WC1 4GB

Our Service Address is:	**You can contact us on:**
14 Broadley Road, Hendon, London, H5 6GF	**Tel: 081 623 0991** **Fax: 081 665 8761**

Edward Electronics
22, Boundary Road
Harrow
London H14 5ON

1220

Date: 3 May 1996

Meter reading		Units	Unit	
Present	**Previous**	**used**	**price**	**Amount £s**
E184755	E170730	14025	9.51p	1,333.78
STANDING CHARGE 1/2/96 TO 30/04/96				58.40
				1,392.18
			VAT	243.63
PAYMENT DUE BY 15 MAY 1996				1,635.81

VAT Reg No 431 3363 81

```
INVOICE
            Edwards Electronics          Tel: 062 249 0896
            22, Boundary Road            Fax: 062 467 8899
            Harrow                       VAT Reg No 488 7657 81
            London
            H14 5ON

Date/Tax Point:  23 March 1996
Order No:  JP 234/PT
To: 45 Electronic Scramblers              £4,657.50

EC State-0-rated            VAT          £0.00

                  Invoice Value  £4,657.50

 Bouverie Electricaine
  45 Rue de Commerce
  Paris 15                              Terms Net 60days
 FRANCE
```

Task 3

The senior accountant of Edwards Electronics has given you the detail that she considers sufficient to compile the VAT return for the quarter ended 31st May 1996. The detail is computer generated and appears below:

```
VAT DETAIL - QUARTER ENDED 31ST MAY 1996


SALES -       DOMESTIC: £68,125  [EXEMPT £18,000
                                   STD £50,125      ]


              OVERSEAS: £36,370
             NON EC:   £21,600
                 EC:   £14,770 [ALL EC-VAT registered]


SALES RETURNS - DOMESTIC: £3,200 [STD-RATED]

PURCHASES/INPUTS - REL TO TAXABLE SUPPLIES        £74,800
                   REL TO EXEMPT SUPPLIES         £12,800
                             MIXED                 £3,100


PURCHASE RETURNS [UK STD-RATED]
 - REL TO TAXABLE SUPPLIES - DOMESTIC £1,800



[ALL FIGURES ARE VAT-EXCLUSIVE]
```

All purchases and other inputs have been obtained in the UK and have been subject to 17.5% VAT except for:

- £15,000-worth of purchase materials imported from Spain and zero-rated by the supplier.

- £8,000-worth of purchases imported from Taiwan. VAT on these imports was deferred at the border.

Both of these inputs were used to service taxable outputs (ie, to make taxable supplies).

Edwards Electronics Ltd agrees with all suppliers and customers to issue appropriate credit and debit notes and fully account for VAT on all returns.

The senior accountant has also told you that there was a VAT over declaration of £890 in the last quarter (ie, that to 29th February 1996) and that relief can now be claimed on UK bad debts that total £1,128.00, standard-rated VAT-inclusive.

You are required to prepare a VAT account for the quarter ended 31st May 1996 and to determine the net amount of VAT payable to, or recoverable from, Customs & Excise for the period.

VAT ACCOUNT - QUARTER ENDED 31ST MAY 1996

```
┌─────────────────────────────────────────────────────────────┐
│ OFFICE NOTE                                                   │
│                                    Edwards Electronics Ltd    │
├─────────────────────────────────────────────────────────────┤
│ WORKINGS:                                                     │
│                                                               │
│                                                               │
│                                                               │
│                                                               │
│                                                               │
│                                                               │
│                                                               │
│                                                               │
│                                                               │
│                                                               │
│                                                               │
│                                                               │
│                                                               │
└─────────────────────────────────────────────────────────────┘
```

Task 4

Make reference to the VAT return that is contained in your textbook. Make a record below [on the office notepad sheet provided], for reference back to the senior accountant, of the amounts to be recorded in boxes 1 to 9 of the return for the quarter ended 31 May 1996.

```
┌─────────────────────────────────────────────────────────────┐
│ OFFICE NOTE                          Edwards Electronics Ltd  │
├─────────────────────────────────────────────────────────────┤
│                            Comment:                           │
│                                                               │
│  BOX 1  [_____]                                   │
│                                                               │
│  BOX 2  [_____]                                   │
│                                                               │
│  BOX 3  [_____]                                   │
│                                                               │
│  BOX 4  [_____]                                   │
│                                                               │
│  BOX 5  [_____]                                   │
│                                                               │
│  BOX 6  [_____]                                   │
│                                                               │
│  BOX 7  [_____]                                   │
│                                                               │
│  BOX 8  [_____]                                   │
│                                                               │
│  BOX 9  [_____]                                   │
│                                                               │
└─────────────────────────────────────────────────────────────┘
```

Note that the figures you have calculated and presented will be taken as **provisional** and subject to any questions or queries you may have on the information you have used to make your calculations. If you have any such questions or queries please note them here:

Task 5

What is the relevance of a tax point?

Task 6

Edwards Electronics Ltd presently accounts for sales VAT by making an appropriate record of each sales transaction in the sales daybook as soon as the associated customer invoice is issued. The Nominal Ledger is updated day-to-day using all daybooks.

The recently-appointed senior accountant is concerned at this fact; she knows that Customs & Excise will expect the VAT on each sales transaction to be accounted for on a date consistent with its tax point. She has passed you a series of documents with the request to confirm the tax point for each sales transaction referred to therein and to further confirm the date at which the company would record the sales VAT in its books under its present system of accounting.

The sales documentation is presented below. Record your findings in this table:

Sale:	Tax Point:	Date that Edwards Electronics would account for VAT in its accounts/Nominal Ledger:
Star Electronics		
George Staicu		
Bill Miller		

Is the senior accountant right to have concern for the way in which Edwards Electronics Ltd accounts for its VAT?

SALES ORDER

Date: 24 March 1996

Customer name: Star Electronics

Existing credit customer: Y /N̶   10% Deposit taken with order: Y̶ / N

Goods:

14 Classic CT14023 Amplifier Units @ £67.50
each ex. VAT

Delivery effected: 29/5   VAT Invoice Issued: 7 April 1996

SALES ORDER

Date: 29 March 1996

Customer name: George Staicu, 7 Broadmead Way
Henley, LONDON, WC4 5OM

Existing credit customer: Y̶ / N   10% Deposit taken with order: Y /N̶

Goods:

1 x Linnemann Slimline TV @ £699.00 incl. VAT

Delivery effected: 19/4   VAT Invoice Issued 19/4 - & full balance of
payment taken on delivery

SALES ORDER

Date: 12 March 1996

Customer name: Bill Miller, 17 Davidge House,
Waterloo Road, LONDON, SE1 4PD

Existing credit customer: Y̶ / N   10% Deposit taken with order: Y̶ / N
See below

Goods:

1 Superstack Hi-fi Unit @ £495.00 incl VAT.
Full payment taken with order

Delivery effected: 22/3/96   VAT Invoice Issued Full receipt/Invoice
issued with order

Task 7

Identify whether the following businesses would be compelled under present legislation to register for VAT or not. Briefly say WHY you make the answers you do. If you feel you are unable to make a decision on the information given, make a note of any further information you would require:

All figures given are annualised amounts.

- Bernoni Costumery and Arts Ltd which has purchases and input expenditure totalling £58,000 [all from UK suppliers] and turnover before considering VAT of £78,000:

Must Register	Need Not Register	More Information Required Before a Decision Can be Taken
☐	☐	☐

Comment/Further Information Required:

- Fakin Costumery and Arts Ltd has purchases and input expenditure totalling £88,000 - all from EC suppliers. Turnover before considering VAT is £128,000, of which £98,000 would be exempt and £30,000 would be taxable:

Must Register	Need Not Register	More Information Required Before a Decision Can be Taken
☐	☐	☐

Comment/Further Information Required:

- Falin Industrials Ltd which has purchases and input tax expenditure totalling £78,000 - £45,000 of which is from EC suppliers. Turnover before considering VAT is £84,000, all of which would be taxable:

	Must Register	Need Not Register	More Information Required Before a Decision Can be Taken
	☐	☐	☐

Comment/Further Information Required:

- Swift Tennis Co which has figures for turnover before considering VAT of £45,000 [UK, of which £16,000 would be exempt anyway] plus £17,000 overseas [outside the EC] and £2,000 overseas [EC]:

	Must Register	Need Not Register	More Information Required Before a Decision Can be Taken
	☐	☐	☐

Comment/Further Information Required:

Task 8

Use a copy of the latest VAT Guide to answer the following questions received in the following note from your office colleague, Wesley Hawkes. **Reference MUST BE MADE to the relevant section in the VAT Guide** but answers may be in short note form (below each numbered item if preferred):

OFFICE NOTE

Edwards Electronics Ltd

Can we offset the VAT borne on the following input expenditure against our output VAT liability to Customs & Excise?:

1   VAT on £875 of meal costs in an expenses claim from Jack Fusher, employee; the meals were taken whilst away from the office attending a training course.

2   VAT on £1,025 of entertainment costs claimed by Jack Fish, Director - the VAT was incurred on a dinner with H Grimes, a sales director with one of our suppliers.

3   VAT included in a till roll for £4,700 from Gladstones General Office Supplies, a cash and carry wholesaler. The products purchased are identified only by product codes on the supplier invoice, although all other necessary VAT detail is given thereon.

Should we generally charge or account for VAT on:

4   Supplies of goods to the UK local authorities? We have recently agreed to supply some products to Bromley District Council and delivery and invoicing will be effected shortly.

5   Goods lost before delivery? We had the recent incident of a Trinyton Hi-fi Unit that was lost (probably stolen) from our warehouse before delivery to the purchaser (Waltons Limited). We could not replace the unit lost and therefore Waltons will not be billed for the product price.

6   Sales of second-hand items? I am aware of the fact that we DO include VAT on our sales invoices presently, but is this correct?

7   Products which we send out to retailers on a sale or return basis (ie, where the retailer either sells the products or has the right to return them to us without charge)?

8   Items gifted to charities? We sometimes make donations of some of our products.

9   Sales to EC customers who are not VAT registered?

10   Sales to non-EC customers?

11   Sales to EC customers who we know are VAT registered, but for whom we do not have the VAT registered number?

Task 9

Respond to the following note (also from Wesley). You can respond by simply recording a 'yes' or 'no' along side each item:

```
┌─────────────────────────────────────────────────────────────────────────────────┐
│ OFFICE NOTE                                                                       │
│                                                      Edwards Electronics Ltd      │
├─────────────────────────────────────────────────────────────────────────────────┤
│                                                                                   │
│ As a general reference and guide for managing our petty cash disbursements, albeit│
│ that they are generally of minor account, would the following presently include   │
│ input VAT (and therefore require a full VAT receipt if we are to offset the VAT    │
│ amounts suffered)?                                                                │
│                                                                                   │
│    •    Office supplies of tea, coffee and sugar?                                 │
│                                                                                   │
│    •    Office supplies of small stationery items?                                │
│                                                                                   │
│    •    Small amounts borne by our employees on fares (eg, on taxis and trains)?  │
│                                                                                   │
│    •    Small amounts of postage?                                                 │
│                                                                                   │
│    •    Supplies of chocolate biscuits?                                           │
│                                                                                   │
│    •    Amounts paid to the office cleaners and Fred the contractor who occasionally│
│         does small electrical and other repairs for us?                           │
│                                                                                   │
└─────────────────────────────────────────────────────────────────────────────────┘
```

HOTLINES

Telephone: 0181 844 0667

Fax: 0181 831 9991

AT FOULKS LYNCH LTD

Number 4, The Griffin Centre
Staines Road, Feltham
Middlesex TW14 0HS

Intended Examination Date: December 96 ☐ June 97 ☐ December 97 ☐	Textbooks	Workbooks	Distance Learning UK MAINLAND ONLY
Foundation - Level 2			
Unit 1 Cash Transactions	£9.95 ☐	£9.95 ☐	£85 ☐
Unit 2 Credit Transactions	£9.95 ☐	£9.95 ☐	£85 ☐
Unit 3 Payroll	£9.95 ☐	£9.95 ☐	£85 ☐
Unit 20 Data Processing	£9.95 ☐ *		£85 ☐
Units 24 - 28 The Business Background	£9.95 ☐ *		£25 ☐
Foundation Level Distance Learning Course			£325 ☐
Intermediate - Level 3			
Units 4 & 5 Capital and Financial Transactions	£9.95 ☐	£9.95 ☐	£85 ☐
Unit 6 Cost Accounting	£9.95 ☐	£9.95 ☐	£85 ☐
Units 7 & 8 Preparing Reports and VAT	£9.95 ☐	£9.95 ☐	£85 ☐
Units 21 & 22 Information Technology	£9.95 ☐ *		£85 ☐
Intermediate Level Distance Learning Course			£325 ☐
	* Combined textbook and workbook.		

POSTAGE		Textbooks	Workbooks	
	UK Mainland	£2.00/book	£2.00/book	Post Free
	NI, ROI & Europe	£5.00/book	£5.00/book	
	Rest of World Standard Air Service	£10.00/book	£10.00/book	UK Mainland Only
COURIER	China & Asia	£20.00/book	£20.00/book	
	West Indies & Africa	£23.00/book	£23.00/book	
	Far East & Middle East	£17.00/book	£17.00/book	
SINGLE ITEM POSTAGE		For orders of 1 item only, add £2.50 (UK/Europe) or £10.00 (Rest of World)		

TOTAL				
	Sub Total £			
Less 24% tax relief for Distance Learning paid for by student only	£			
	Postage £			
	Total £			

DELIVERY DETAILS

Student's name (print)

Delivery address

Postcode

Telephone Daytime

Telephone Evening

Note: All delivery times subject to stock availability.
Signature required on receipt.

Allow: 5 working days - work address (UK mainland)
10 working days - home address (UK mainland)
10 working days - Overseas Courier Service
6 weeks - Overseas Standard Air Service

PAYMENT OPTIONS

1. I enclose Cheque/PO/Bankers Draft for £_____

    Please make cheques payable to AT Foulks Lynch Ltd.

2. Charge Access/Visa Account Number

    ☐☐☐☐☐☐☐☐☐☐☐☐☐☐☐☐☐☐

    Expiry Date ☐☐☐☐

    Signature   Date

DECLARATION
I agree to pay as indicated on this form and understand that AT Foulks Lynch Ltd Terms and Conditions apply (available on request). I understand that AT Foulks Lynch Ltd are not liable for non-delivery if the Rest of World Standard Air Service is used.

Signature   Date

All details correct at time of printing.   *Source: ATWBJ6*